THE STAIRWAY TO LIFE

THE STAIRWAY TO LIFE:

An Origin-of-Life Reality Check

Change Laura Tan
Rob Stadler

ISBN: 978-1-7341837-0-2 (paperback)
ISBN: 978-1-7341837-1-9 (Kindle)

THE STAIRWAY TO LIFE

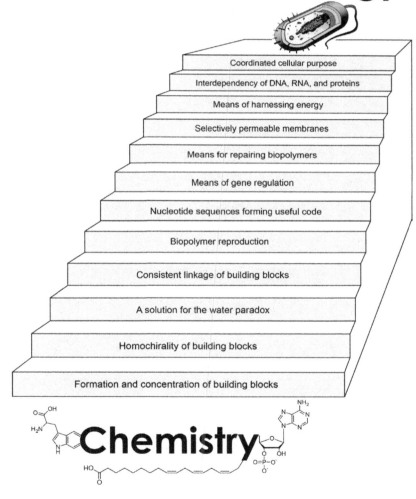

Biology

- Coordinated cellular purpose
- Interdependency of DNA, RNA, and proteins
- Means of harnessing energy
- Selectively permeable membranes
- Means for repairing biopolymers
- Means of gene regulation
- Nucleotide sequences forming useful code
- Biopolymer reproduction
- Consistent linkage of building blocks
- A solution for the water paradox
- Homochirality of building blocks
- Formation and concentration of building blocks

Chemistry

Table of Contents

Introduction

Among the myriad of dubious theories from the distant past, the theory of spontaneous generation has enjoyed exceptional endurance. Belief in the spontaneous formation of living organisms, without the need for seeds or eggs or parents of any kind, was already prevalent at the time of Aristotle, but he is largely credited with formalizing the concept. From his book *The History of Animals*, from the fourth century BC:

> With animals, some spring from parent animals according to their kind, whilst others grow spontaneously and not from kindred stock; and of these instances of spontaneous generation some come from putrefying Earth or vegetable matter, as is the case with a number of insects, while others are spontaneously generated in the inside of animals out of the secretions of their several organs [1].

Due to his work, the theory of spontaneous generation is also known as "Aristotelian abiogenesis," where the more general term "abiogenesis" refers to life arising naturally from nonliving matter.

Over the next two millennia, support for the spontaneous generation of larger organisms like lions, rats, and mice eroded very slowly, retreating over centuries to bastions of support for spontaneous generation of smaller forms of life. Support remained strong for spontaneous generation of insects. Rotting flesh was believed to be a source of spontaneous generation of maggots, and this belief survived without formidable opposition until the time of Francesco Redi, an Italian physician, biologist, and poet. In 1668, he published his magnum opus, *Experiments on the Generation of Insects*, in which he demonstrated experimentally that maggots did not arise from decaying flesh when placed in a jar covered by gauze. He concluded:

> Although content to be corrected by anyone wiser than myself, if I should make erroneous statements, I shall express my belief that the Earth, after having brought forth the first plants and animals at the beginning by order of the Supreme and Omnipotent Creator, has never since produced any kinds of plants or animals, either perfect or imperfect; and everything which we know in past or present times that she has produced, came solely from the true seeds of the plants and animals themselves, which thus, through means of their own, preserve their species ([2], 160).

Despite the powerful insight that Redi's simple experiment provided, proponents of spontaneous generation merely retreated to smaller scales, continuing to support spontaneous generation of microscopic life. Redi's 1668 publication was contemporaneous with Robert Hooke's *Micrographia*, wherein a coarse compound microscope led to the first descriptions of a cell. Hooke also observed mold growing on leather but was unable to observe any form of "seed" and therefore concluded that the mold had generated spontaneously, either from natural or artificial heat. Spontaneous generation of microscopic life continued to enjoy strong support over the next two centuries; indeed, simply soaking hay in pure water generated a veritable zoo of microscopic life with no trace of seed, egg, or progenitor of any form. A noteworthy late proponent of spontaneous generation was Erasmus Darwin, the grandfather of Charles Darwin. His book *The Temple of Nature* (an unconventional mixture of poetry and science, published posthumously in 1803) summarized his beliefs ([3], Canto I. 1. 227):

> Hence without parent by spontaneous birth
> Rise the first specks of animated earth.

For which he provided the following explanation in an appendix:

> From the misconception of the ignorant or superstitious, it has been thought somewhat profane to speak in favour of spontaneous vital production... There is therefore no absurdity in believing that the most simple animals and vegetables may be produced by the congress of the parts of decomposing organic matter, without what can properly be termed generation, as the genus did not previously exist; which accounts for the endless varieties, as well as for the immense numbers of microscopic animals.

In the mid-nineteenth century, the French Academy of Sciences offered a prize to anyone who could experimentally support or refute spontaneous generation of microscopic life. In 1859, Louis Pasteur conducted an elegant experiment with meat broth in swan-necked bottles, showing that nothing would grow in a bottle of boiled broth unless particles entered from the air. This provided cogent evidence that even microscopic life could not arise spontaneously. Pasteur concluded:

> Never will the doctrine of spontaneous genera-
> tion recover from the mortal blow of this simple
> experiment. There is no known circumstance in
> which it can be confirmed that microscopic beings
> came into the world without germs, without par-
> ents similar to themselves [4].

Yet Pasteur's confident assertion was flatly denied. Like a phoenix, abiogenesis immediately began a new life, although re-treating yet again to a smaller scale. You may recognize that the year of Pasteur's experiment (1859) was the same year of another renowned scientific accomplishment: the publication of Darwin's *On the Origin of Species*. Undoubtedly greatly influenced by his grandfather Erasmus, Charles Darwin maintained a belief, or at least a hope, that life could arise spontaneously. The former Aristotelian abiogenesis implied a rapid arrival of an intact organism without seed, egg, or parents. Darwin's abiogenesis retreated further to the molecular level, applied only to the first life to arrive on the planet, and required an expanse of time. Darwin expressed this view in an 1871 letter to his friend Joseph Hooker:

> It is often said that all the conditions for the first
> production of a living organism are now present,
> which could ever have been present—But if (and
> Oh! what a big if!) we could conceive in some warm

little pond with all sorts of ammonia and phosphoric salts,—light, heat, electricity etc., present, that a protein compound was chemically formed, ready to undergo still more complex changes, at the present day such matter would be instantly devoured, or absorbed, which would not have been the case before living creatures were formed [5].

Darwin's espousal of this new form of spontaneous generation, and its role in his overall theory of evolution, has drawn new battle lines in a conflict that remains very active today. Darwin is joined by every atheist because the absence of god necessitates a naturalistic explanation for the start of life, even if it happened on some other planet. Francis Crick, the codiscoverer of the structure of DNA, eventually warmed to abiogenesis, although his initial pessimism on the likelihood of abiogenesis led him to propose the theory of panspermia (the possibility that life on Earth came from elsewhere in the universe) [6]. NASA strongly supports abiogenesis, recently forming the Prebiotic[1] Chemistry and Early Earth Environments Consortium to unite experts across the world to study the origin of life [7, 8]. Bill Nye affirmed his alliance in a book chapter called "The Sparks That Started It All," where he states, "The origin of life just requires some raw material that could allow the spark of life to emerge" ([9], 285). Those who control public school curricula in the United States tend to support abiogenesis, perhaps somewhat out of fear of legal action, because special interest groups argue that even questioning abiogenesis is tantamount to promoting religion, in violation of the Establishment Clause of

---

1. The term "prebiotic" refers to the period before life existed.

the U.S. Constitution.[2] Many modern biology textbooks are clearly written to encourage millions of students to accept abiogenesis. The following are a few examples from well-known textbooks:

> Because Pasteur's data were so conclusive—meaning that there was no other reasonable explanation for them—the results persuaded most biologists that the all-cells-from-cells hypothesis was correct. However, you will see that biologists now have evidence that life did arise from nonlife early in Earth's history, through a process called chemical evolution ([10], 4).

> Life began when organic molecules assembled in a coordinated manner within a cell membrane and began reproducing. Whether the organic molecules formed on Earth or elsewhere and were transported to Earth within meteors is an open question ([11], 507).

> Although life as we would identify it has not been created in the lab from scratch, these results support the hypothesis that life could have been formed spontaneously on Earth ([12], 248).

> Life arose from nonlife via chemical evolution ([13], 3).

---

2. The First Amendment to the Constitution of the United States of America states: "Congress shall make no law respecting an establishment of religion." This is the "Establishment Clause," intended to prohibit the government from establishing a national religion. Publicly funded schools therefore cannot encourage belief in a particular religion.

On the other side of the conflict are people who do not believe that life originated from purely natural processes, thus requiring at least a minimum of supernatural intervention. They remain unconvinced by claims that science supports abiogenesis. For the time being, those who doubt abiogenesis have the simple but powerful element of scientific observation on their side because indeed no one has ever observed life arise from nonlife. As biochemist Michael Denton said, "Considering the way the prebiotic soup is referred to in so many discussions of the origin of life as an already established reality, it comes as something of a shock to realize that there is absolutely no positive evidence for its existence" ([14], 261).

The only known way to create a new cell (the basic unit of life) is from an existing cell.

Perhaps with one exception...

This book examines new insights into abiogenesis, as prompted by a substantial milestone in molecular biology: the creation of "the first self-replicating species that we've had on the planet whose parent is a computer" [15]. This milestone was announced in May 2010 by Craig Venter and his colleagues—the culmination of over fifteen years of work, more than forty researchers, and an estimated forty million dollars [15, 16].

Believing that "what I cannot build, I cannot understand" [16], the Venter team set out to understand life by synthesizing life, and Venter's claim of a "self-replicating species whose parent is a computer" provides a strong suggestion that he synthesized de novo life. For some supporters of abiogenesis, Venter's work implied that spontaneous initiation of life is a real possibility.

Publication of the first self-replicating synthetic life (a single-celled organism named *Mycoplasma mycoides* JCVI-syn1.0, but better known as *Synthia*) sent ripples throughout the scientific community [17–24]. The prestigious journal *Nature* asked eight biology experts about the implications for science and society [17].[3] President Obama asked the White House Bioethics Commission to study the issues raised by synthetic biology and report back to him within six months [20]. The environmental protection nonprofit group Friends of the Earth asked the Environmental Protection Agency and the Food and Drug Administration to fully regulate all synthetic biology experiments and products [21]. In the words of Georgios Zenonos (a neurosurgeon at the University of Pittsburgh) and Jeong Eun Kim (a neurosurgeon at Seoul National University), "Not only did Venter's audacious statements and claims of 'synthetic' life mark a triumph of biotechnological ingenuity, but they also undermined the foundations of religions, cosmotheories, cultures, ethics, and law, questioning the essence of life itself" [18]. Arthur Caplan, a professor of bioethics at the University of Pennsylvania and one of the eight synthetic biology experts, said that Venter's achievement "undermines a fundamental belief about the nature of life that is likely to prove as momentous to our view of ourselves and our place in the Universe as the discoveries of Galileo, Copernicus, Darwin and Einstein" [17]. Such an impactful milestone deserves careful attention.

In Part I of this book, we briefly review Venter's approach to synthetic life, with an emphasis on applications to abiogenesis. Although Venter's work does not directly address abiogenesis, it does provide powerful insights into the required constituents, complexity, and information content of the simplest forms of life. Part I may be too technical for some readers. If so, we recommend

---

3. These are eight people with eight opinions, as glimpsed from the titles of their essays: "The Power and the Pitfalls" by Mark Bedau, "Now Let's Lower Costs" by George Church, "'Bottom-up' Will Be More Telling" by Steen Rasmussen, "The End of Vitalism" by Arthur Caplan, "Synthesis Drives Innovation" by Steven Benner, "Nature's Limits Still Apply" by Martin Fussenegger, "Got Parts, Need Manual" by Jim Collins, and "Origin of Life Just Got Closer" by David Deamer [17].

reading the chapter summaries and advancing to Part II. In Part II, we combine the learnings from Venter with other recent discoveries in biology to arrive at a fundamental set of requirements for life, organized into a structure called "the Stairway to Life." The Stairway to Life provides a new perspective on abiogenesis because each of the twelve required steps is profoundly unlikely to occur in a prebiotic world, and the improbabilities of each step must be multiplied to arrive at the infinitesimal overall likelihood of abiogenesis. Part III then discusses the implications of the Stairway to Life in an effort to resolve the conflict over abiogenesis.

Part I.
Lessons from
Synthetic Life

Omnis cellula e cellula.
(All cells come from cells.)

—Rudolf Virchow

Chapter 1
Recipe for a Self-Replicating Cell

All things are created twice; first mentally; then physically. The key to creativity is to begin with the end in mind, with a vision and a blue print of the desired result.

—Stephen R. Covey [25]

Synthetic chemistry and baking have much in common. Available recipes provide a straightforward path to a goal, whereas the creation of novel recipes requires patience, persistence, and skill. Working with "off-the-shelf" ingredients saves time and effort but may diminish the eventual sense of accomplishment, whereas creation "from scratch" dramatically increases the effort but enhances the resulting sense of accomplishment.

When Craig Venter and his team set out with bold ambition to create the world's first synthetic living cell, the only known recipe came from existing life. They began by considering possible approaches to arrive at a new recipe for life. They could have approached the problem in a manner that no lucid chef would consider: mixing random assortments from a lengthy list of ingredients into millions of individual cocktails, then subjecting them to a wide variety of heating protocols and selecting the best of the results after each step in the process. This would mimic abiogenesis, where the "from-scratch" ingredients would be organic building blocks and the recipe would include the natural conditions of a prebiotic Earth. Or they could have attempted to design a cell from scratch, synthesizing the essential ingredients according to human designs and assembling them into a proper cellular structure via a recipe of human intelligence, with living organisms as a model. A third, less ambitious approach would take shortcuts by borrowing "off-the-shelf" ingredients: first determining the minimum set of genes required for life, then assembling a genome from a collection of those existing genes from different organisms, then combining the genome with a minimal selection of other cellular components, resulting in a minimally viable life-form. A final option, notably the least ambitious, would copy the genome from a single existing organism and substitute this genome for the existing genome in a living cell, thus making exclusive use of the existing recipe for life and all "off-the-shelf" ingredients from existing life. A brief consideration of the challenges posed by each of these four approaches will lead to a strongly preferred approach: the same approach that Venter selected.

Repeating Abiogenesis in the Lab

Can we synthesize a living cell by mixing all the basic chemicals that all organisms use, including all the nucleotides, amino acids, lipids, carbohydrates, and various ions, and allowing them to interact with each other randomly, trusting that natural selection[4] will sculpt a living organism? To put this another way, can we

---

4. Natural selection is the differential survival of and/or reproduction of classes of entities that differ in one or more characteristics ([26], 6).

transition from chemistry to biology within the confines of a laboratory experiment?

For over sixty years, millions of biology students have studied the Miller-Urey experiment: a simple mixture of H_2, NH_3, CH_4, and H_2O gases subjected to electric discharges, resulting in the production of some amino acids (the building blocks of proteins).[5] Biology textbooks have a habit of embellishing these results, providing the impression that laboratory-generated life is within reach. The hype that followed the Miller-Urey experiment led to a memorable quotation published in 1960: "At a recent meeting in Chicago, a highly distinguished international panel of experts was polled. All considered the experimental production of life in the laboratory imminent" [27].

In the years since Miller-Urey, investigations into the molecular mechanisms that constitute life have revealed previously unimagined layers of complexity for even the most simplistic forms of life, whereas prebiotic laboratory synthesis of biomolecules has made minimal progress. These efforts have sharpened our appreciation of the challenges in generating life from simple chemicals. This topic will be addressed in Part II of this book. Nobody makes a cake by randomly mixing ingredients and randomly heating the mixtures, and the simplest living organism is extraordinarily complex compared to a cake. Given this, Venter wisely avoided such a difficult and uncertain pathway to synthesize life.

Synthesizing by Human Design

The central dogma of molecular biology involves the transfer of information from DNA to protein (Figure 1). Following years of painstaking research, humans now have a good understanding of the genetic code that lies at the foundation of this central dogma.

---

5. Chapter 7 provides additional details.

Cells use the genetic code to translate sequences of nucleotides into sequences of amino acids. Humans can also use the genetic code to translate information backward from a desired protein to a corresponding nucleotide sequence of DNA. We can also synthesize DNA with any desired sequence, at least sequences of modest lengths. Therefore, at first glance, it would seem reasonable to design novel proteins that carry out the desired metabolic and reproductive functions of a synthetic living organism and assemble the corresponding DNA into a genome.

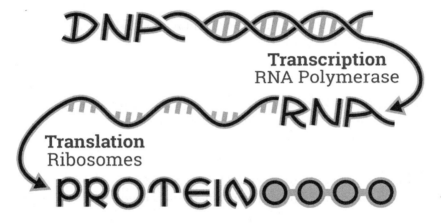

Figure 1. A simplistic view of the central dogma of molecular biology. The information in DNA resides in a linear sequence of four nucleotides. The nucleotides on one side of DNA are each paired with complementary nucleotides on the other side to make a sequence of base pairs. The base pairs form the "rungs" that make up the double-helix "ladder" of the DNA molecule. Through the process of transcription, the information in DNA is copied to messenger RNA by the enzyme RNA polymerase. Ribosomes then perform translation, converting the messenger RNA code into the sequence of amino acids that form a protein.

However, an understanding of the central dogma of molecular biology and the ability to synthesize a desired DNA sequence are dramatically different from de novo design of useful genetic information. A four-year-old can identify the letters of the alphabet, but synthesizing the letters into a Shakespearean tragedy requires a much more advanced understanding, creativity, and mastery. Designing useful genetic information requires a complete understanding of the impact of the new information on the overall organism and its environment. For the production of proteins, this involves: 1) regulation of when and how much of the protein is produced (this regulation can be mind-bogglingly complex, involving dozens of other proteins and their interactions with DNA), 2) delivery of the produced protein to the appropriate place inside or outside of the cell, 3) knowledge of the three-dimensional structure that a given sequence of amino acids will form,[6] and 4) knowledge of the interaction of the protein with all other molecules.

To date, successful examples of designed modifications to DNA and proteins have all involved starting with the DNA of existing genes and attempting minor modifications or repairs to known errors, mixing parts of different genes to generate chimeras, or transplanting genes from one species to another. These modifications should be followed by extensive testing to assess the full impact on the organism and its environment. The untimely death of Jesse Gelsinger in 1999, following an early form of gene therapy for an enzyme[7] deficiency, serves as a painful reminder. Although we have made great progress in genetic engineering, we

---

6. Although much recent progress has been made in predicting the 3-D folding of proteins [28, 29], proper 3-D folding of proteins often requires the assistance of other proteins called chaperones, and improperly folded proteins can be deadly—a lesson learned from prions.
7. Enzymes are proteins that facilitate biochemical and metabolic reactions.

have neither the knowledge nor the resources to design, synthesize, and test a complete living cell.

Venter wisely passed on attempting to synthesize a complete cell by human design. In fact, the only novel pieces of DNA code that the Venter team included in the *Synthia* genome is what they called watermarks [16, 30]. These watermarks consisted of nonfunctional DNA sequences that encoded phrases in the English language by representing English letters with short DNA sequences. One of the watermarks contained the code for converting the series of A, C, T, and G nucleotides into the English alphabet. The other watermarks contained a website address for the project, the names of the forty-six key contributors who synthesized the *Synthia* cells, and three quotations: "To live, to err, to fall, to triumph, to recreate life out of life"; "See things not as they are, but as they might be"; and "What I cannot build, I cannot understand" [16]. This is impressive work, but inventing DNA sequences that code for functional proteins is a herculean effort compared to creating nonfunctional watermark DNA sequences. Because the DNA watermarks that Venter added to *Synthia* serve no practical purpose for the organism yet require energy to copy during replication, we can predict that they will degrade over generations from accumulated mutations, or they will be expelled completely from the *Synthia* genome to yield a more efficient organism. Like spam in your inbox, the DNA watermarks that Venter added to *Synthia* serve no practical purpose for the organism, interfere with normal activity, and will likely be deleted in short order.

Synthesizing from a Minimal Gene Set

A minimal gene set contains the smallest number of required genes to sustain a functional organism, one that can self-replicate in the presence of all necessary nutrients and in the absence of any environmental stress [31]. Two popular methods have been used to estimate the minimal gene set required for a self-replicating cell. One involves identifying a core set of genes shared by different existing organisms—those fundamental for a broad range of life. The other systematically inactivates individual genes in an organism to determine which genes are essential for survival and/ or reproduction.

The first method aims at identifying homologous genes— that is, genes that have similar sequences but are found in different organisms. Homologous genes are generally thought to have evolved from a common ancestral gene. Therefore, evolution would predict that all organisms share the remnants of a core set of essential genes. After complete sequencing of the first two bacterial genomes, a comparison of the 1,727 protein-coding genes of *Haemophilus influenzae* and the 468 *Mycoplasma genitalium* genes identified 240 homologous genes between the two [32]. This suggested that those 240 genes might constitute a minimal genome for life. However, when the number of included prokaryotic[8] genomes increased to one hundred, the number of homologous genes decreased to sixty-three [33]. Finally, with the inclusion of one thousand prokaryotic genomes, the number of homologous genes became zero—not a single protein-coding gene was conserved across the thousand prokaryotes that were compared [34]. Therefore, searching for homologous genes failed to determine the minimal gene set required to make a self-replicating cell. This finding also casts doubt on the belief that a common ancestor underlies all prokaryotes because they do not all share a fundamental set of essential genes.

The second method to arrive at a minimal genome strives to identify genes that are essential by assessing survivability of an

---

8. All of life is organized into three domains: Bacteria, Archaea, and Eukarya. "Prokaryotes" include bacteria and archaea.

organism after inactivating or deleting individual genes [35–44]. One such study suggested that *Mycoplasma genitalium*, the free-living organism that has the smallest genome, contains 425 essential genes (382 protein-coding genes and 43 RNA-coding genes) [36]. However, this is an inappropriately low estimate because the work did not account for synthetic lethality.[9]

The finding that at least four hundred genes are required for the survival and propagation of even the simplest cells came as somewhat of a surprise to those who imagine a simple start to life. This also casts substantial doubt on the possibility of creating a self-replicating cell by random chance.

A minimal set of essential genes for life, collected from a variety of organisms, has not been identified. Therefore, the Venter team did not attempt to construct a first synthetic self-replicating cell from a minimal gene set.[10] Lacking other options, Venter took the fourth and final choice—synthesizing the genome of an existing organism and transplanting it into an existing cell, the least glorious but the only feasible choice of the four.

Synthesizing the Genome of a Living Organism

The Venter team began with synthesis of the genome of *M. genitalium* because it is the free-living organism with the smallest known genome: a circular genome of 580,070 base pairs (bp) [30,

---

9. In synthetic lethality, the loss of a single gene may not be lethal for an organism, but simultaneous loss of that gene together with another nonessential gene results in death [45–50]. Therefore, minimal gene sets cannot be obtained via single-gene knockouts. For example, demonstration of a viable organism after knocking out only gene A and subsequent demonstration of a viable organism after knocking out only gene B could lead to the conclusion that neither A nor B is essential for life. However, knocking out both genes A and B could lead to death, so each combination of gene knockouts must also be evaluated.
10. Later experiments from the Venter team showed that the minimal essential gene approach did not work. They admitted that their "biggest design challenge has been synthetic lethal pairs" [51].

52]. However, they soon discovered that a smaller genome did not necessarily imply easier synthesis of a self-replicating cell. *M. genitalium* reproduces too slowly (once every sixteen hours), leading them to redirect their focus to another type of mycoplasma. *Mycoplasma mycoides* reproduces every eighty minutes but has more than one million base pairs in its genome, almost twice as many as that of *M. genitalium* [30]. Venter synthesized a slightly modified version of the *M. mycoides* genome and activated it by placing it into a closely related organism, *Mycoplasma capricolum*, resulting in *Synthia*. We will describe how the Venter team synthesized the genomic DNA of *Synthia* in Chapter 2 and how they activated the genome in Chapter 3.

Chapter 1 Summary:

1. Even the simplest known autonomously reproducing organism, *M. genitalium*, requires the choreographic functioning of hundreds of genes to survive and reproduce.

2. The gene contents of various organisms differ greatly. Among the first thousand prokaryotic genomes that were sequenced, not a single protein-coding gene is conserved across all genomes [34].

3. Of the four potential routes to synthesizing a self-replicating cell—1) synthesizing by design, 2) synthesizing by random arrangement of the basic building blocks, 3) synthesizing from a minimal set of genes, and 4) synthesizing the genome of an extant organism—Venter chose the last one, the only feasible approach.

Chapter 2
Synthesis of the *Synthia* Genome

Although existing laboratory methods could synthesize short segments of DNA from individual nucleotides, Venter's team was the first to accomplish the monumental task of synthesizing an entire genome. In this chapter, we provide a high-level overview of Venter's approach to genome-scale synthesis. Our goal is to avoid heavy technical content while clearly presenting the challenges Venter faced in synthesizing a known genome. His approach provides important insights into the concept of spontaneous generation of life and into claims of common ancestry for all life.

Venter's efforts to produce *Synthia* cells involved the "cast of characters" listed in Table 1. This table includes nicknames for organisms to simplify the description of their roles. To summarize, the Venter team designed the *Synthia* genomic sequence with the help of a computer, starting with the known genomic sequence of *M. mycoides* ("*Myco*") and adding the watermarks mentioned previously as well as small segments of DNA from yeast and *E. coli*. In total, the genomic sequence of *Synthia* included 98.55% of unmodified *Myco* DNA, 0.43% of watermarks inserted by humans, 0.08%

of DNA that *E. coli* happened to insert (via transposons[11]) while it was making copies of DNA segments, and 0.94% of DNA copied from a yeast cloning vector[12] (Figure 2). The 0.94% of DNA copied from a yeast cloning vector was needed to facilitate the synthesis, identification, and isolation of the genome via the conscription of molecular machinery from living organisms. The team then employed a multistep process to produce the genome in a laboratory, according to the design stored in the computer, and placed it in a preexisting living cell, eventually replacing the cell's native DNA.

Table 1: The "cast of characters" involved in the synthesis of *Synthia*.

Organism	Domain	Role	Nickname
Mycoplasma mycoides JCVI-syn1.0	Bacteria (prokaryote)	The desired "synthetic" cell.	*Synthia*
Mycoplasma genitalium	Bacteria (prokaryote)	Initially of interest because it has the smallest known genome of a free-living organism but subsequently rejected because of slow reproduction.	
Mycoplasma mycoides	Bacteria (prokaryote)	Provided the vast majority of the genomic DNA sequence for *Synthia*.	*Myco*
Escherichia coli	Bacteria (prokaryote)	Produced copies of (i.e., amplified) short segments of the *Synthia* genome.	*E. coli*
Saccharomyces cerevisiae	Eukarya	Synthesized long segments of the *Synthia* genome.	Yeast
Mycoplasma capricolum	Bacteria (prokaryote)	Donated cytoplasm and membranes; served as the host cell for the *Synthia* genome.	*Capri*

---

11. A transposon is a movable DNA element that, when inserted at some locations within a gene, will disrupt the function of that gene.
12. A cloning vector is a small piece of DNA taken from a virus, a plasmid, or a cell that can be stably maintained in an organism and into which a foreign DNA fragment can be inserted for the purpose of making many copies (cloning).

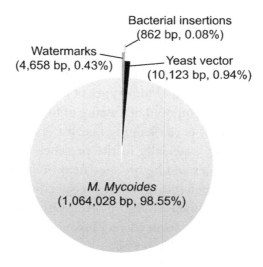

Figure 2. The composition of *Synthia* genomic DNA. "bp" = base pairs.

Using a divide-and-conquer strategy, the desired *Synthia* genome was split into 1,078 consecutive, overlapping DNA segments, each containing 1,080 base pairs. Each segment, now called a "1 kb cassette" (kb = kilobase pair), was subsequently divided into between fifteen and twenty overlapping fragments of DNA, or "oligonucleotides" ("oligos").[13] Each oligo was then synthesized separately, and the full-length *Synthia* genome was assembled by combining the oligos into larger segments of DNA, then successively combining the larger segments into the full-length genome. Blue Heron, a gene-synthesizing company [30], synthesized the single-stranded DNA oligos for Venter's work and assembled them into the 1kb cassettes.[14]

---

13. Blue Heron, personal communication.
14. Since no technical details from Blue Heron or the Venter team are available for these two steps, we provide a summary of the common practice of synthesizing and assembling oligos.

Synthesizing the Overlapping Oligos

Laboratory synthesis of DNA is complex and almost entirely unnatural, yet the process provides a sobering illustration of the challenges that must be overcome to produce DNA. A desired oligo, composed of a string of four types of nucleotides, somewhat resembles a necklace composed of a string of four specific types of beads. Oligo synthesis is challenging because the beads naturally resist proper linking, especially in the presence of water. In living organisms, complex and highly specific protein enzymes force proper linkages between individual beads (specifically, the natural form of nucleotides shown in Figure 3A). Without the enzymes, forcing the nucleotides to form correct linkages requires some impressive chemical jujitsu maneuvers.

Purified, highly modified monomers: Laboratory production of oligos starts with highly modified monomers—not the natural form of nucleotides as in Figure 3A but nucleotides where all the reactive functional groups have been selectively inactivated or activated, as in Figure 3B. The monomers must also have extreme purity because any impurities would rapidly decrease the yield of the desired oligo. The monomers are manufactured, stored, and used in the absence of water and air [53, 54]; residual water poisons the desired reactions and is the most common complication in oligo synthesis [55]. Highly purified versions of the modified monomers are readily available today from laboratory supply companies but would not have been available in a prebiotic world (as discussed in Chapter 7).

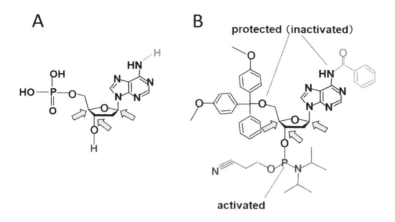

Figure 3. *A*, normal deoxynucleotide (adenosine monophosphate) as found in living organisms. *B*, modified deoxynucleotide for laboratory synthesis. To avoid undesired side reactions, all the functional groups that should not react are rendered unreactive (i.e., protected) by attaching protecting groups, while the functional groups that should react are activated. The arrows highlight chiral centers.

Pure chirality: In DNA, the atomic bonds surrounding many of the carbon atoms result in an asymmetric molecular structure. As a result, the molecule and its mirror image are not superimposable (see Figure 4). This property, known as "chirality," is discussed in detail in Chapter 8. Just as your left and right hands are not superimposable, these chiral locations can exist in right- and left-handed forms that are not interchangeable. Each nucleotide of DNA has three chiral locations and therefore could exist in any of eight (i.e., 2 X 2 X 2) possible chiral configurations (in Figure 3, the three chiral centers in each nucleotide are highlighted with arrows). However, every nucleotide in the DNA of every known living organism on the planet, including the 6.4 billion nucleotides in almost every cell in your body, has the same chirality when functioning properly. Without the help of enzymes found only in living organisms, synthetic production of individual nucleotides from simple component molecules would always result in equal proportions of the possible chiral configurations, known as a racemic mixture. However, the synthetic production of DNA in a laboratory requires pure chirality because any contamination with incorrect chirality would render the synthesized products unusable. Therefore, the purchased building blocks for laboratory synthesis must include only the correct chirality. The chirality, the selectively activated and inactivated states, and the purity of the building blocks are luxuries unavailable outside of living cells or the controlled laboratory environment.

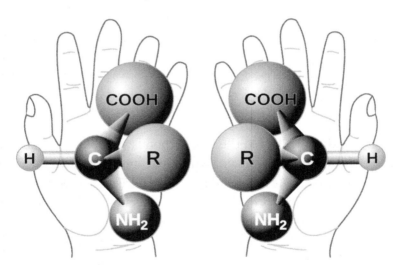

Figure 4. Two nonsuperimposable chiral forms of a generic amino acid, where *R* indicates a variety of possible organic structures.

Precise linkage of monomers: During formation of an oligo, controlled chemical reactions activate the desired locations for chemical bonding. In this way, only specific locations are primed to react, and they react exactly as desired to extend the growing oligo. This requires a lengthy sequence of precise reactions that introduce a new monomer, force its proper attachment to the growing oligo, block any oligos that failed to accept the new monomer, and wash away any unreacted monomers so they do not interfere with the introduction of the next desired monomer. Upon completion of all reactions to produce the desired oligo, all protecting groups are removed to yield the final product. For the detail-oriented reader, Figure 5 describes the five essential steps to link each monomer to a growing oligo [56, 57]. In a prebiotic world, long chains of consistently linked monomers are extraordinarily unlikely, as discussed in Chapter 10.

Avoiding errors: Even with careful and selective activation and protection of functional groups, interfering side reactions cannot be avoided, and errors in the DNA sequence are relatively common. In a published report, oligos up to about one hundred nucleotides can be routinely synthesized with error rates of approximately one in two hundred nucleotides [56], although more recent results likely exceed this performance. Because of the errors and the incomplete yield of each reaction cycle, the yield of the final desired product decreases with each added nucleotide and the length of synthesized oligos must be limited. Upon completion of the synthesis, high-performance liquid chromatography is applied to separate the desired oligos from undesired molecules that were produced by erroneous reactions. For these reasons, each 1kb cassette had to be divided into multiple overlapping oligos, mostly in the range of sixty-five to one hundred base pairs.[15]

---

15. Personal communication with Blue Heron.

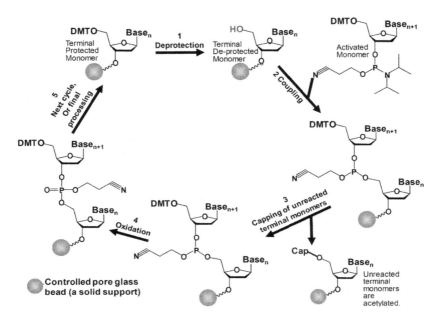

Figure 5. An oligo synthesis cycle. (Warning: this diagram is only for the detail-oriented reader!) Laboratory synthesis of oligos proceeds in the opposite direction of DNA synthesis in living organisms. The first nucleoside (a nucleotide without its phosphate group) is attached to a solid phase support (filled circle), and its hydroxy group is activated or deblocked by the removal of the protection group DMT (step 1: deprotection). The resulting free-hydroxy group will attack the phosphite moiety of the next nucleoside phosphoramidite (step 2: coupling). Terminal monomers that fail to add the next nucleotide are blocked from further chain elongation (step 3: capping). The newly formed linkage is next oxidized because it is not natural and is of limited stability under the conditions of oligo synthesis (step 4: oxidation). The resultant product then serves as the starting material for the next cycle of base addition. Upon the completion of the oligo chain assembly, all the protecting groups are removed and the desired oligo is finally freed from the solid support.

Combining the Oligos

Laboratory synthesis of DNA cannot begin to approximate the accuracy of natural replication of DNA in cells—the natural process for *E. coli* has an error rate of approximately 1 in 1,000,000,000. The cellular process of DNA production is not only incredibly accurate, but it is also incredibly fast (about one thousand nucleotides per second in *E. coli*). If DNA was scaled up to be one meter in diameter, the protein-based molecular machinery that replicates DNA "would move at approximately 600 km/hr (375 mph), and the replication machinery would be about the size of a FedEx delivery truck. Replicating the *E. coli* genome would be a 40 min, 400 km (250 mile) trip for two such machines, which would, on average make an error only once every 170 km (106 miles)" ([58], 295). And all this occurs automatically in a cell that is just two microns in length, at our normal body temperature of 37°C.

Therefore, in the next step, Venter borrowed enzymes found only in living cells (ligase or polymerase [56]) to combine the overlapping oligos into 1kb cassettes [30]. Live *E. coli* cells, with their highly accurate, fast, and inexpensive DNA replication machinery, were then conscripted to copy the resultant 1kb cassettes. The Venter team then verified the DNA sequence of all cloned 1kb cassettes to ensure accuracy [30].

The researchers next isolated the 1kb cassettes and used yeast cells to assemble each group of ten cassettes into 10kb intermediates. The resulting 10kb intermediates were then transferred back into *E. coli* so they could be produced in large quantity.

Venter's use of both *E. coli* and yeast to produce the 10kb intermediates required some impressive genetic engineering. An *E. coli* origin of DNA replication, a yeast origin of DNA replication, a bacterial selectable marker gene, and a yeast selectable marker gene had to be employed in the production of the 10kb intermediates. Cellular replication of DNA begins at a specific sequence of DNA that indicates the origin of DNA replication. But *E. coli* and yeast have distinct origins of DNA replication; the two are not compatible. As a result, Venter had to employ both an *E. coli* origin of DNA replication and a yeast origin of DNA replication. The selectable marker genes were inserted to filter out unwanted products. The bacterial marker gene was an antibiotic resistance gene so that an antibiotic could be administered to remove any *E. coli* that did not have the added resistance to the antibiotic. The yeast marker gene was for the production of an essential nutrient, such that any extraneous yeast that could not produce that nutrient would die when the nutrient was not provided as a source of food. The bacterial marker gene operated under the control of a bacterial gene promoter,[16] while the yeast marker gene operated under the control of a yeast gene promoter.

Like the origins of DNA replication, the promoters of bacterial and yeast genes have different structures, are recognized by different proteins, and are not exchangeable. The absolute incompatibility between prokaryote (e.g., *E. coli*) and eukaryote (e.g., yeast) origins of replication and promoters, as well as DNA replication, transcription, and translation machineries, stands as a largely unrecognized challenge to the evolutionary view that the two share a common ancestor.

After transferring the 10kb intermediates into *E. coli*, the Venter team then isolated the 10kb intermediates and assembled them into 100kb intermediates in yeast. The yeast produced quantities of each 100kb intermediate. The 100kb intermediates were then purified from yeast and assembled into the full-length genome in yeast. This full-length *Synthia* genome could then be produced in quantity and, in the presence of selection media,

---

16. A promoter is a DNA sequence at which RNA polymerase binds and initiates transcription.

maintained in yeast. With this, the Venter team had accomplished the largest DNA synthesis to date.

A Genome Can Do Nothing on Its Own

DNA, even one million base pairs of information-packed DNA, is incapable of living on its own. Without the help of membranes and thousands of accompanying molecules, DNA cannot generate energy, perform metabolic functions, reproduce itself, properly fold or untangle itself, protect itself from degradation, selectively surround itself with desirable molecules, or exclude undesirable molecules. Thus, almost no one involved in origin-of-life research believes that DNA could have been responsible for starting the first life.

The yeast cells that were required to assemble the full-length *Synthia* genomic DNA from 1kb cassettes contained all the required ingredients for the life of yeast and for the synthesis of the complete *Synthia* genome, yet they were incapable of producing a living *Synthia* cell. As we mentioned previously, the molecular machinery for DNA replication, transcription, and translation are incompatible between eukaryotes (e.g., yeast) and prokaryotes (e.g., *Myco* or *Synthia*).

Here is a useful analogy: you acquire the complete set of specifications to make a smartphone and you provide the specifications along with all necessary raw materials like silicon, lithium, and glass to a group of well-educated individuals with diverse backgrounds. You then ask them to produce a working smartphone and give them all the time that they want. But because they do not have and cannot create the manufacturing equipment (which requires an entirely different set of specifications and expertise), they have no ability to turn silicon into the required integrated circuits, no way to turn lithium into rechargeable batteries, no way to code the specified software into the device, etc. If you then provided the full set of equipment necessary for manufacturing automobile tires, they may be able to make a bit more progress—for example, the computers involved in tire manufacturing could be repurposed to some extent to code the specified smartphone software—but they still could not produce a smartphone. The only way to produce a working smartphone would be to make use of an existing smartphone factory with all the essential machinery that enable silicon wafer fabrication, microcircuit assembly, battery production, etc. In this analogy, the complete specifications for the smartphone are the *Synthia* genome. The smartphone factory is a living *Synthia* cell. The raw materials are the phospholipids, nucleotides, amino acids, etc. that are necessary for life. The equipment for manufacturing tires is the living yeast cell (a eukaryote). A living yeast cell that contains the *Synthia* genome and all that a yeast cell needs to survive cannot produce a living *Synthia* cell (a prokaryote).

Chapter 2 Summary:

1. The Venter team constructed a very large *Synthia* genomic DNA, starting with reagents that were extremely pure, had consistent chirality, and were selectively activated and inactivated.

2. Protein enzymes and other components found only in living organisms were required for synthesis of the *Synthia* genome.

3. *E. coli* (a prokaryote) and yeast (a eukaryote) rely on DNA replication and transcription machineries that are not exchangeable, yet controlled manipulation of these incompatible processes was required to make a *Synthia* genome.

4. None of the DNAs made by the Venter team (or anyone else) could replicate themselves, nor could they make RNA, a protein, or a living cell without existing cellular components designed to utilize the information in those DNAs. Even yeast cells, which were used to assemble and maintain the *Synthia* genomic DNA, were incapable of reading or using the *Synthia* genomic DNA to make a *Synthia* cell.

Chapter 3
Decoding the Code

Having synthesized the complete *Synthia* genome, the next step was to combine the DNA with the required cellular components to arrive at a fully functional cell. For this, the Venter team again had to seek help from existing life-forms. They conducted a search for the perfect recipient cell, a type of "surrogate parent" that would provide matching cellular structures and molecular machinery to work with the *Synthia* genome. Similar to organ transplantation, the challenge involved finding the right match to avoid early death. Unlike organ transplantation, where matching refers to immune response, the matching in this case related to code recognition. Code (i.e., information) can only fulfill its purpose if it can be interpreted.

Transcribing the Codes

In living cells, the first step of decoding the information in a genome is the transcription of its genes into RNA.[17] In its simplest form, transcription requires the coordinated action of at least three essential components. A promoter region is necessary (although it may not be sufficient) for a segment of DNA to be recognized as a gene. A second segment of DNA is necessary (although it may not be sufficient) to serve as a transcription termination signal. Finally, transcription machinery made of multiple proteins must recognize the promoter and terminator and transcribe the gene. For this reason, the production of the *Synthia* genome required bacterial genes to be placed under the control of a bacterial promoter and yeast genes to be placed under the control of a yeast promoter (recall that yeast is a eukaryote).

Translating the Codes

The second step of decoding the information in a genome involves the translation of its messenger RNA (mRNA) transcripts into a protein, a process that occurs via ribosomes. Translation requires the coordinated action of at least three components: 1) The mRNA needs to have a translation initiation site, which includes a starting codon[18] and surrounding sequences to establish the correct reading frame and the protein-coding region.[19] Each mRNA has three potential reading frames. Consequently, the same mRNA could

---

17. Often, the RNA formed by transcription is messenger RNA (mRNA), but some nonprotein-coding genes, such as ribosomal RNA (rRNA), transfer RNAs (tRNAs), and microRNA (miRNA) will also be transcribed. These nonprotein-coding RNAs do not directly code for proteins but commonly take part in the production or regulation of proteins.
18. A codon is a set of three nucleotides that form a unit of genetic code.
19. A reading frame is a specific way of dividing the bases of an mRNA into consecutive, nonoverlapping sets of three bases. Each set of three bases is translated into an amino acid in the protein-coding region.

code for different proteins or no protein, depending on the context. 2) The host cell must have translation machinery that can recognize the starting codon. 3) A correct translation termination site must be recognizable by the translation termination molecules to release the mRNA and the translated protein product from the ribosome.

The starting codon may differ between yeast, *E. coli*, and mycoplasmas (such as *Myco*, the source of 98.55% of the *Synthia* genome). In yeast, the starting codon is AUG;[20] in *E. coli*, the starting codon can also be GUG, UUG, AUU, AUC, AUA, or CUG. Mycoplasmas add UUA to the set of *E. coli* starting codons [59]. The proper starting codon is not sufficient to direct the translation machinery where to start translation. The correct nucleotide sequence and the correct three-dimensional structure of the mRNA around the starting codon, as well as RNAs and proteins within the cell, are all critical for correct translation initiation. For example, the codon AUG can be read as a translation initiation site, as an amino acid methionine in the middle of the protein, or as portions of two other codons if it is located in an alternative reading frame. It can even serve an entirely different purpose or be ignored if it is located outside of the protein-coding region of a gene. Also, bacteria and eukaryotes differ in their way of defining and recognizing translation initiation sites. Thus, the starting codons in the *Synthia* genome may not be properly interpreted by yeast or *E. coli*.

Another relevant difference pertains to the specific codon UGA. In *Myco*, UGA codes for the amino acid tryptophan, whereas UGA in yeast or *E. coli* RNA codes for termination of translation. Consequently, even if a *Synthia* gene were transcribed in

---

20. Here, A = adenine, U = uracil, G = guanine, and C = cytosine, the four nucleotides of RNA.

yeast or *E. coli* and translation of the resulting mRNA could get started, protein production would stop when the UGA codon for tryptophan appeared.

Biology textbooks like to simplify life by providing a single table of codons for translating DNA to proteins. But in fact, the National Center for Biotechnology Information (NCBI) currently lists thirty-three different genetic code tables for a variety of life-forms [59]. The differences are subtle, but even subtle differences produce fatal incompatibilities between life-forms. For example, if mycoplasmas are ancestors to bacteria or yeast, one must explain how the codon UGA could switch from coding for the amino acid tryptophan to coding for the end of translation without killing the organism. As this coding transition occurred, every protein that contains tryptophan coded by UGA would suddenly be truncated at that point, causing certain death. Furthermore, bacteria, archaea, and eukaryotes each have their own unique way to define and recognize the starting codon and to discriminate the starting codon from other appearances of the same codon. As a result, an organism that operates according to one genetic coding-decoding system cannot survive under a different genetic coding-decoding system. The near impossibility of maintaining life while changing the genetic coding-decoding strategy therefore poses another challenge for the assumed common ancestry of all life.

Finding a Match

Creation of a living *Synthia* cell required a nearly perfect match between the codes in the *Synthia* genome and the codes that the recipient cell expected. As mentioned above, the translation initiation and termination mechanisms of *Synthia* are not compatible with yeast or *E. coli*. Although yeast was able to assemble and replicate the *Synthia* genomic DNA, there are significant differences between the methods that yeast and *Synthia* employ to determine if a segment of DNA is a gene and to determine what gene products it encodes. Thus, living yeast was not able to decode the *Synthia* genome. The only living organisms with a sufficiently similar coding-decoding system to serve as the recipient cell (or a genome acceptor) were other mycoplasmas.

Myco and *Capri* share more than 99% identity for the 79 core proteins involved in gene translation, as well as their ribosomal DNA [60].[21] Consequently, *Capri* cells were able to duplicate the *Synthia* genome, recognize the promoters of *Synthia* genes, transcribe *Synthia* genes, and recognize the translation starting sites, translation stopping sites, and *Synthia* codons. In short, the *Capri* RNAs and proteins were not only able to replicate the synthesized *Synthia* genome but also to decode and execute the instructions encoded in this genome. *Capri* was therefore selected as the host cell for the *Synthia* genome.

The process of activating the *Synthia* genome in recipient *Capri* cells was like upgrading the operating system on a computer. The "hardware" (proteins and RNAs) to execute the instructions was sufficiently similar between *Myco* and *Capri* to allow a successful "reboot" after replacing the *Capri* "software" (genome) with the *Synthia* "software" (genome). In contrast, significant hardware differences exist between *Myco* and *E. coli* and between *Myco* and yeast (like the hardware differences between Mac and PC), such that the replacement of an *E. coli* or yeast genome with the genome of *Synthia* would result in a "crash" (like replacing MacOS on Mac hardware with the Windows operating system).

Venter's work emphasized the selectivity of different types of cells to different forms of information. Code has no value unless it can be properly decoded. Cellular mechanisms for decoding DNA

---

21. Ribosomal DNA is the DNA that codes for the ribosomal RNA, which is an essential component of ribosomes—the molecular machines that synthesize proteins by translating messenger RNAs.

are very specific and complex: the machinery for DNA replication, transcription, and translation are all taxonomically specific (i.e., they are not universal or conserved across all of life but rather are largely incompatible between different life-forms, especially between bacteria and eukaryotes). Similarly, decoding mechanisms have no value without code. Therefore, only simultaneous arrival of the code and the corresponding decoding mechanisms could lead to life.

Chapter 3 Summary:

1. Code has no value without decoding mechanisms and vice versa. Both appropriate coding and appropriate decoding mechanisms are critical for making a self-replicating cell, and they must arrive simultaneously.

2. Compatibility between code and the decoding machinery is essential for life, yet code and decoding machinery are typically incompatible between different forms of life.

Chapter 4

So Close, Yet So Far Away

Close only counts in horseshoes and hand grenades.

—Frank Robinson, *Time* magazine, July 31, 1973

Having synthesized the desired DNA for *Synthia* and having found the perfect "surrogate parent" for the birth of *Synthia*, one would expect a swift and satisfying conclusion to Venter's journey. However, a few hidden hurdles remained. These hurdles provide insight into the complexity of life and the implausibility of its spontaneous generation.

Restriction Enzymes

Restriction enzymes—specialized enzymes that cut any DNA that matches a specific pattern [30, 61]—created another hurdle for the Venter team. Restriction enzymes serve as security guards in cells, destroying any foreign DNA. The organism's own DNA is not destroyed because it has a specific pattern of methylation[22] provided

---

22. DNA methylation is a temporary modification of either cytosine or adenine bases by the addition of a methyl group. Methylation can modify the activity of a DNA segment without modification to the DNA sequence.

by the organism's own methyltransferase enzymes. Foreign DNA can only sneak past the security system if it is disguised by a similar pattern of methylation. Restriction systems are another reason why transplanting foreign DNA into a cell is similar to organ transplantation. The security system of a human (i.e., the immune system) will reject an organ that is not well matched; likewise, the security system of a cell (i.e., the restriction system) will reject any DNA that is not well matched.

Because *Capri* is so similar to *Myco*, DNA made in *Myco* cells is readily accepted by a *Capri* cell. The vast majority of the *Synthia* genome came from *Myco*, so one might expect easy passage through the "security system" of *Capri*. However, the actual *Synthia* DNA was produced by yeast, not by *Myco*, and yeast-made DNA is quickly destroyed by the restriction enzymes in *Capri*. This led to an unexpected failure for Venter's team.

This situation is steeped in irony. The *Synthia* DNA is almost a perfect match for *Capri* cells yet was rejected. The required enzymes (methyltransferases) to allow the safe passage of the *Synthia* DNA into *Capri* were encoded in the *Synthia* genomic DNA, so the yeast that produced *Synthia* genomic DNA actually contained the instructions to properly disguise the DNA, but the yeast could not follow the instructions because the promoters for the *Synthia* methyltransferase genes could not be recognized by the yeast transcription machinery and because the genetic codons used in yeast are not compatible with those used in *Myco*. However, fortunately, the yeast was also incapable of producing the restriction enzymes coded in the *Synthia* genome because those enzymes may have destroyed the yeast's own DNA and the *Synthia* genome contained within the cells. The restriction system poses quite a challenge to the spontaneous generation of life.

The Venter team had to overcome this challenge by either methylating the *Synthia* DNA in vitro (using enzymes extracted from *Capri* or *Myco*) or by deleting the *Capri* restriction enzyme gene. Both approaches were successful. Thus, in addition to the barriers generated by the incompatibility of prokaryotic and eukaryotic molecular machineries of DNA replication, transcription, and translation described in Chapters 2 and 3, other barriers exist between different organisms that would be quite difficult to overcome by natural means.

A Single Base Pair Can Determine the Life or Death of a Cell

Yet another hurdle that the Venter team had to overcome—or more accurately, had to submit to—was the necessity of essential genes [30]. An essential gene, as the name implies, codes for a function that the cell simply cannot live without. Any missing essential genes, or even a simple mutation in an essential gene that interferes with its function, will result in the death of the organism. Venter's team, despite carefully checking all the 1kb cassettes for errors, had the misfortune of overlooking the deletion of a single base pair—one mistake out of a million. Unfortunately, this single base-pair deletion occurred in an essential gene called *dnaA*. The *dnaA* gene produces a protein that binds to the prokaryotic origin of DNA replication, making it essential for prokaryote reproduction. The deleted base pair resulted in a frameshift[23] and a completely dysfunctional gene, thus ensuring that *Synthia* could not reproduce.

Here again we perceive a touch of irony. The *Synthia* genome (containing the broken *dnaA* gene) was itself successfully replicated in yeast because the yeast had different proteins to take the

---

23. A frameshift is a type of mutation involving insertion or deletion of a number of nucleotides that is not divisible by three. Because each set of three nucleotides specifies a codon, a frameshift mutation results in a completely different translation compared to the original.

place of DnaA in the process of DNA replication.[24] The recipient cells, *Capri*, were also able to replicate the defective *Synthia* genome using functional DnaA proteins made from the functional *Capri dnaA* gene. However, after the *Capri* genomic DNA was removed from the cloned cell and the functional DnaA proteins in the cloned cells had deteriorated, no functional DnaA could be produced from the remaining *Synthia* genome, resulting in *Synthia* cells that could not reproduce. Thus, both yeast and *Capri* performed their roles in duplicating the DNA for *Synthia*, including perfect duplication of the error in the *Synthia dnaA* gene, but this resulted in a *Synthia* genome that could not reproduce itself—like a sterile mule produced by a horse and a donkey.

One might be inclined to suggest that the organism could simply "evolve" to fix this mutation on its own via a corrective mutation that luckily replaced the missing base. However, without the essential function of *dnaA*, the organism cannot reproduce, so evolution is a nonstarter. This simple observation should provoke some contemplation on the hypothesized pathway to the evolution of any essential genes, such as the more than four hundred essential genes needed for the simplest known life-forms. If a single missing base pair in one essential gene can be so devastating and cannot be repaired by random mutations and natural selection, what process could be responsible for the origin of *dnaA* and the hundreds of other essential genes?

Note that the bacterial cells simply followed their programmed behavior: they did not "care" whether the synthesized *Synthia* genome resulted in living cells or not. Nor were they capable of pinpointing or correcting the error that rendered them incapable of

---

24. In eukaryotes like yeast, the function of DnaA is replaced by the origin recognition complex (ORC), which is composed of six different proteins.

reproducing. Only Venter's team cared—and only they, the able human intellects, identified and restored the missing base pair.

The two hurdles described here reveal potential barriers or discontinuities between life and nonlife, as well as between different life-forms on Earth, a topic we will discuss further in Part II.

Chapter 4 Summary:

1. Restriction systems create a barrier between different life-forms.

2. Each essential gene is indispensable for the life of an organism. An organism cannot exist until all its essential genes are available.

3. A combination of human intellect, existing genomic information from living organisms, and existing molecular machinery from living organisms was required to overcome the barriers to create *Synthia*.

Chapter 5

The Culmination of Fifteen Years of Work

Having overcome numerous hurdles, some during the synthesis of more than one million base pairs of DNA and some following the synthesis, we now reach the culmination of fifteen years of work for Venter and his team. The synthetic *Synthia* genome was transplanted into live *Capri* cells in a bath, and a small fraction of the *Capri* cells incorporated the new genome. These cells then contained both their native genome and the *Synthia* genome. The remaining tasks were to remove the native *Capri* genome and separate out the newborn *Synthia* cells. Before cell division, the *Capri* cells with both genomes could duplicate both genomes using the *Capri* DNA replication machinery. For the cells that duplicated both genomes, the added *Synthia* genome was a metabolic burden, requiring twice the normal resources for the process of genome duplication. Therefore, these cells had reduced fitness relative to the native *Capri* cells in the bath.

Upon cell division, some daughter cells contained only the synthetic *Synthia* genome, some contained only the *Capri* genome, and some contained both genomes. This mixture of cell types would normally be very challenging to separate, but Venter wisely designed a powerful filter into the DNA for the purpose of selecting only the desired *Synthia* cells. Venter added an antibiotic resistance gene to *Synthia*, which does not exist in either the donor genome (*Myco*) or the recipient genome (*Capri*), thus enabling cells with the *Synthia* genome to survive and reproduce in the presence of the antibiotic tetracycline. Thus, the cells containing only the *Capri* genome were destroyed when all cells were placed in tetracycline media. The remaining cells with both genomes either split into *Synthia*-only genome cells in subsequent generations or maintained both genomes and were eventually outcompeted by the *Synthia* cells (because maintaining and duplicating two genomes is metabolically unfavorable).

In the absence of the antibiotic selection, it is quite reasonable to assume that the wild-type *Capri* cells would have dominated—in part because they did not deal with the extra burden of maintaining and copying two genomes and in part because very few cells accepted the added *Synthia* genome. Thus, the final steps to obtain *Synthia* cells required artificial selection, not a natural process. The resulting separated *Synthia* cells were then able to live and reproduce on their own. At last, Venter's team had accomplished their goal.

As with any great accomplishment, some will amplify the importance of the findings, while others will minimize their importance. Venter's team referred to the accomplishment as "the first self-replicating species that we've had on the planet whose parent is a computer" [16]. Clyde Hutchison, a member of Venter's team, said, "To me the most remarkable thing about our synthetic cell is that its genome was designed in the computer and brought to life through chemical synthesis, without using any pieces of natural DNA." In contrast, Caltech geneticist David Baltimore said, "To my mind Craig [Venter] has somewhat overplayed the importance of this...He has not created life, only mimicked it" [17]. Because more than 99% of the total *Synthia* genome, 100% of its functional genes, and all molecular structures and machinery were derived from naturally existing organisms, Venter's claim that the organism had a computer as a parent is certainly questionable (see [62] for a detailed discussion). Compared to Venter's computer, even sperm donors are substantially more engaged in parenting.

Ultimately, interpretation of Venter's accomplishment will be left to the individual. Our goal is to apply the lessons learned from Venter's efforts to the concept of spontaneous generation of life. We learned that each step of the synthesis of *Synthia* required processes that could only be performed by existing living organisms or an intelligent agent. The intelligent agent began the work with a goal in mind, a design, and a preferred approach. The intelligent agent designed the artificial selection and "hijacked" specific components from living organisms. The application of artificial selection was essential in several steps (e.g., whenever a segment of *Synthia* DNA was cloned in *E. coli* or yeast and was amplified and isolated). This artificial selection ensured that the weak were preferred over the strong—the opposite of natural processes. With the exception of oligo synthesis, molecular machines from living organisms were applied in each step to accomplish the goal. Materials found only in living organisms were required for every step in the process, starting with the desired chirality of every basic chemical building block. Venter's work had to overcome the fundamental incompatibility between different life-forms, which calls into question the common ancestry of all of life. Finally, we also discussed essential genes. The observations that the simplest known life-forms have approximately four hundred essential genes and that a single-base deletion in one of the essential genes in *Synthia* resulted in death call into question the possibility that any natural process could start life.

Therefore, without human interference and the borrowing of information and molecular machines from existing life, one could conclude that nature and all the chemical and physical laws could not make a self-replicating *Synthia* cell. Perhaps Venter's greatest achievement is revealing some of the requirements and challenges of building a self-replicating cell. We will explore this further in Part II.

Chapter 5 Summary:

1. Synthesis of the *Synthia* genomic DNA required a combination of human engineering, components borrowed from existing lifeforms, and artificial selection—a process that opposed natural selection by ensuring survival of the weak and destruction of the strong to remove all undesired intermediate products.

2. Venter's experiment revealed some of the requirements and challenges to building a self-replicating cell, which should encourage skepticism toward belief in abiogenesis.

3. *Omnis cellula e cellula* ("All cells come from cells," an observation by Rudolf Virchow) is maintained. *Synthia* clearly came from other cells.

Part II.
The Overlooked
Reality of Life's
Complexity

We have before this become acquainted with the simplest of all species of organisms in the monera, whose entire bodies when completely developed consist of nothing but a semifluid albuminous lump; they are organisms which are of the utmost importance for the theory of the first origin of life. But most other organisms, also, at a certain period of their existence—at least, in the first period of their life in the shape of egg-cells or germcells, are essentially nothing but simple little lumps of such albuminous formative matter, known as plasma, or protoplasma.

—Ernst Haeckel, 1883 ([63], 330)

Chapter 6
The Stairway to Life

The storyline has been repeated again and again throughout history, boldly proclaiming that we have failed to learn from the past: humans always approach a biological phenomenon by first assuming that it is far simpler than reality. Even as the layers of actual complexity are revealed, we repeatedly fool ourselves into thinking that the most recently understood layer will be the last. Perhaps our naive assumptions of simplicity come from our desire to achieve dominion over all of life. Ernst Haeckel believed that life began spontaneously through natural processes, and his belief likely amplified his incorrect assumptions about the simplicity of life. In *The History of Creation*, he referred to Monera (the name of an obsolete taxonomic kingdom that has been replaced by the domains of Archaea and Bacteria—the domains that include *Myco*, *Capri*, *Synthia*, and *E. coli*) as

> Organisms which are, in fact, not composed of any organs at all, but consist entirely of shapeless, simple, homogeneous matter. The entire body of one of these Monera, during life, is nothing more than a shapeless, mobile, little lump of mucus or

> slime, consisting of an albuminous combination of carbon. Simpler or more imperfect organisms we cannot possibly conceive ([63], 184).

Perhaps we could excuse Ernst Haeckel for making such a bold yet extraordinarily naive statement about the complexity of cells late in the nineteenth century, just as we could excuse Aristotle for concluding that animals could arise spontaneously from nonliving matter in the fourth century BC. However, the same grievous underestimation of the complexity of life is committed daily in the twenty-first century.

Countless biology textbooks describe the Miller-Urey experiment and others like it as strong evidence that life began spontaneously. This argument seemingly equates the simplicity of a handful of amino acids (formed by a natural process) with the unimaginable complexity of living organisms. This is like finding sand and concluding that microprocessors (computer chips based upon silicon) must be able to assemble spontaneously. Indeed, the chasm between simple organic molecules and living organisms is frequently dismissed in a single sentence. Take, for example, this quote from a popular biology textbook: "The first spark of life ignited when simple chemical reactions began to convert small molecules into larger, more complex molecules with novel 3-D structures and activities" ([10], 104). In his 2014 book, *Undeniable*, Bill Nye similarly applies "the spark of life" to dismiss complexity: "The origin of life just requires some raw material that could allow the spark of life to emerge" ([9], 285). Walt Disney made a movie about a wooden puppet that turned into a boy through a spark of life. Perhaps such fantasy inspired our current biology textbooks and Bill Nye because these statements are certainly not based on scientific evidence or rational thought.

In *The Vital Question*, a 2015 book that Bill Gates praised as "an amazing inquiry into the origins of life," biochemist Nick Lane expects his readers to join him in dismissing the great complexity separating simple building blocks and living cells:

> The formation of organic matter from H_2 and CO_2 is thermodynamically favoured under alkaline hydrothermal conditions, so long as oxygen is excluded…This means that organic matter should form spontaneously from H_2 and CO_2 under these conditions. The formation of cells releases energy and increases overall entropy! ([64], 114)

The average reader of *The Vital Question* may not have noticed the colossal leap that occurred in the last sentence, where Lane equates spontaneous formation of organic building blocks with the spontaneous formation of cells. This could indeed be possible if cells were "nothing more than a shapeless, mobile, little lump of mucus or slime, consisting of an albuminous combination of carbon," as thought by Haeckel in the late nineteenth century, but each new year of research exposes previously unimagined layers of cellular complexity, even among the simplest known forms of life.

Bestselling author Dan Brown, in his 2017 book *Origin*, includes a respected scholarly character Robert Langdon who concludes, "Life arose spontaneously from the laws of physics" ([65], 402). Addy Pross, a professor of chemistry at Ben Gurion University, concludes the following in his 2012 book, *What is Life?*: "Life then is just the chemical consequences that derive from the power of exponential growth operating on certain replicating systems" ([66], 164). Jeremy England, a professor of physics at MIT who also happens to appear in Dan Brown's *Origin*, similarly sweeps all the complexity of life under the rug with one sentence:

"You start with a random clump of atoms, and if you shine light on it for long enough, it should not be so surprising that you get a plant" [67]. Carl Sagan offered similar words, which are strikingly discordant with all observable evidence: "The origin of life must be a highly probable affair; as soon as conditions permit, up it pops!" [68].

Daily news articles on astronomy and astrobiology barrage us with suggestions that life probably exists on other planets. These articles lead us to believe that the simple discovery of water on a planet virtually guarantees the spontaneous formation of life.

A reality check is long overdue. The fantastic complexity of all known life-forms stands in stark contrast to what our schools are teaching, what some scientists believe, and what popular media suggests.

The grand cloning effort of Craig Venter provided considerable practical insight into the challenges of transitioning from chemistry to biology at the start of life. Even though his work relied extensively on components from existing life-forms, pure concentrated starting materials, and carefully designed and controlled reaction pathways, he encountered several unforeseen obstacles that greatly extended the duration and cost of the effort. The full scope of abiogenesis requires exclusively abiotic materials and processes for every step—many orders of magnitude more difficult than Venter's work.

Required Steps

From our current understanding of life, even the simplest forms of life, we can envision a sequence of required steps to achieve abiogenesis, starting from chemistry (raw natural building materials and simple reactions) and ending with biology (a living cell). Figure 6 lists some of the required steps, using the helpful analogy of a stairway. Undoubtedly, this figure also oversimplifies the requirements for abiogenesis because some steps are certainly missing. The specific ordering of steps in Figure 6 should not be viewed as an attempt at dogma. We do not wish to be sidetracked by debates over the order of the steps. The important point is that each step is required in the process of abiogenesis.

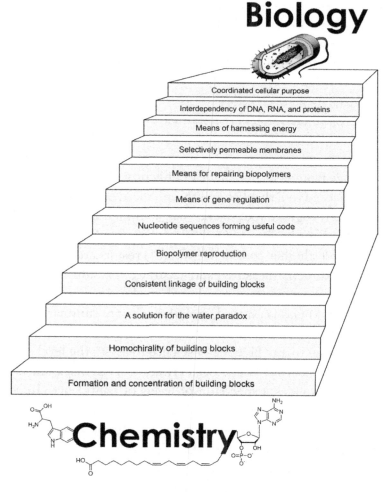

Figure 6. The Stairway to Life.

In the next twelve chapters, we will explore each step in The Stairway to Life. Each chapter will describe the difficulties in accomplishing a given step through natural abiotic processes, with each subsequent chapter describing the new difficulties of the next step, *under the assumption that all prior difficulties have been overcome.* But one cannot lose sight of the forest for the trees—ultimately, the improbabilities of each step are multiplied (not added) on top of preceding steps, such that reaching the top of the stairway becomes mathematically, scientifically, and rationally untenable.

Assessing the Quality of Evidence

As we explore each step in the Stairway, we will review some of the available evidence. When considering the strength of scientific evidence, it is important to distinguish evidence that provides high confidence from evidence that can only provide low confidence.

Science is a tool that has greatly enhanced our lives, yet it is important to recognize that science has its limitations. As described in Rob Stadler's book, *The Scientific Approach to Evolution* [69], science provides higher confidence when 1) results are repeatable, 2) results are directly measured and accurate, 3) results are obtained through prospective, interventional study, 4) assumptions are minimized, 5) bias is avoided, and 6) results are summarized with sober judgment, not amplified or extrapolated. These six criteria can be applied to any practice of science to assess the level of confidence of a scientific result. Each criterion is not black-and-white but rather provides a spectrum of levels of confidence. In some fields of science, the six criteria simply cannot be met despite the best efforts and creativity of scientists. As a simple example, direct measurements on black holes are very limited. We have learned about black holes mostly through their indirect action on other objects and from their lack of electromagnetic radiation. Black holes also cannot be studied via prospective interventions; you cannot bring a black hole into the laboratory and run tests on it. Limitations like these reduce confidence in our conclusions and should be openly disclosed when summarizing results.

When these six criteria are applied to the study of abiogenesis, a crisis of confidence immediately results. Looking at each criterion in turn:

1. The origin of life is the antithesis of repeatable; it is an event that supposedly occurred on one occasion, about four billion years ago. Even if modern laboratory experiments could create life from nonlife, we would have no confidence that the conditions of the laboratory experiments were consistent with those of the early Earth.

2. Our efforts to scrape together trace remnants of evidence of this event leave us with measurements or observations that are extremely indirect.

3. The words "prospective" and "interventional" simply cannot be considered when attempting to study a hypothetical event from four billion years ago.

4. The application of assumptions is essential and seemingly unconstrained, as assumptions are the only way to fill in what is unknown and unknowable from four billion years in the past.

5. Bias is often rampant because of the deadly combination of minimal hard evidence and dogmatic, bipartisan beliefs. The influence of bias and assumptions far exceeds the influence of evidence related to abiogenesis because the

evidence is so weak but the conviction of the researchers is so strong.

6. Finally, the only way to summarize abiogenesis research with sober judgment is to admit that confidence and clarity are unachievable; the best that science can provide with respect to origin-of-life research is a suggestion of possibility. The introductory quotations in this chapter from Ernst Haeckel, Bill Nye, Addy Pross, Jeremy England, and Carl Sagan demonstrate the opposite of sober judgment: proclamation of powerful support for abiogenesis in the absence of evidence.

In stark contrast, by providing ever-increasing insight into the mechanisms of existing life, especially for the simplest known forms of autonomously reproducing life, science can provide high confidence in stating a minimal set of requirements for life (i.e., Figure 6). Recent studies on the mechanisms of existing life commonly meet all six of the requirements for high-confidence science: 1) results are repeatable, 2) results are directly measured and accurate, 3) results are obtained through prospective, interventional study, 4) assumptions are minimized, 5) bias is avoided, and 6) results are summarized with sober judgment, not amplified or extrapolated. Thus, our level of confidence in specifying what abiogenesis must accomplish is quite high, while our level of confidence in any proposed mechanism of abiogenesis is extraordinarily low.

Chapter 7

Formation and Concentration of Building Blocks

Every construction project begins with the assembly of building materials. For all known life on Earth, a fundamental set of building materials is required, including amino acids, sugars, nitrogenous bases, and phospholipids. Production of these building blocks via natural processes (referred to as "prebiotic synthesis") is essential to achieve the first step in the Stairway to Life (Figure 6). Thousands of published papers have attempted to address prebiotic synthesis, each eager to claim an important contribution and disinterested in discussing limitations. Many describe chemical reactions like: A + B produces C, under conditions D, E, and F. Here, C is a required building block for life (or is similar to a building block). D, E, and F are a series of specific conditions required for the reaction to occur. For example, D could be a requirement that no oxygen is present, E could be a requirement that a specific catalyst is present, and F could be a requirement of at least one hundred degrees Celsius. Some proposed reactions require more specific conditions than others. Almost without exception, the published studies start with highly purified and concentrated reactants A and B, purchased from laboratory supply companies. In contrast, nature gravitates toward higher entropy: complex mixtures of a wide variety of diluted chemicals. Pure and concentrated reactants are highly unnatural. The claims of success in producing a building block C under controlled laboratory conditions must be interpreted in light of the real challenges: How can we know that A and B were present on the Earth four billion years ago as pure and concentrated reagents? How can we know that the controlled laboratory conditions D, E, and F represent actual conditions from four billion years ago?

Rampant claims of synthesis under "prebiotic conditions" appear throughout the literature, and debates ensue over whose experimental conditions are "more prebiotic." The absence of any confidence or consensus in the hypothetical conditions on Earth four billion years ago fuels the debate. Leslie Orgel, a well-known advocate for abiogenesis, proposed three requirements to claim prebiotic conditions:

1. It must be plausible, at least to the proposers of abiotic synthesis, that the starting materials for a synthesis could have been present in adequate amounts at the site of synthesis.

2. Reactions must occur in water or in the absence of a solvent.

3. The yield of the product must be "significant" at least in the view of the proposers of the synthesis [70].

The fact that two of the three criteria rely upon the opinion of those who proposed the synthesis may help explain why the criteria are so commonly met. Imagine if the Food and Drug Administration (FDA) based their approval process for a new drug on one criterion: the drug is safe and effective in the view of the drug manufacturer. This would take us back to the days of snake oil salesmen.

As we review some of the more promising results in prebiotic synthesis (essentially claims that the first step on the Stairway to Life has been attained under laboratory conditions), bear in mind that the inherent assumptions, bias, and extraordinarily retrospective nature of prebiotic synthesis implies that this area of science is nearly powerless to distinguish reality from wishful thinking. Desperation in the search for evidence often encourages one to perceive any form of evidence, no matter how unlikely, as compelling. The field of prebiotic synthesis is not and cannot be built upon the foundation of confidence that we have come to expect from modern science, such as the science that supports the safety and efficacy of any pills that you took this week. Prebiotic synthesis can only provide a vanishingly thin veneer of confidence that conceals the vast uncertainty behind these results.

Amino Acids

In 1953, Stanley Miller produced the first experimental prebiotic synthesis result in a paper titled "A Production of Amino Acids Under Possible Primitive Earth Conditions" [71]. He produced glycine, α-alanine, and β-alanine from a gas mixture of H_2, NH_3, CH_4, and H_2O combined with electric discharges. Notice that the mixture of gases (called a "reducing" atmosphere) contained no oxygen. Mixing oxygen with methane or hydrogen and applying a spark might have prematurely ended Miller's career.

The electrical discharges that helped to produce larger molecules like amino acids could also destroy them. The larger molecules were therefore protected from the electrical discharge—a setup that seems rather unlikely in a prebiotic world. To Miller's credit, the words "Possible Primitive Earth Conditions" in his title appropriately reflect the low confidence in the environmental conditions of long ago. These conditions were suggested by the Soviet biochemist Alexander Oparin in his book *The Origin of Life*, first published in 1924 [72]. Many have interpreted the Miller-Urey experiments as strong evidence for abiogenesis. The Stairway to Life (Figure 6) puts this into a proper perspective: Miller-Urey only partially completed the very first step in the Stairway to Life. We are left to wonder why modern biology textbooks choose not to provide a more sober perspective.

After the death of Stanley Miller in 2007, Jeffrey Bada, a former graduate student of Miller, reanalyzed some of Miller's old experimental samples—dried residues kept in vials for fifty years. He employed modern equipment that was orders of magnitude more sensitive at detecting trace molecules [73]. When he included an experiment that also added H_2S to the reducing environment, he found ten of the twenty common amino acids of life, among a predominance of amino acids, amines, and other molecules that are not found in living organisms [74]. As with other papers on prebiotic chemistry, the sparse chemical products that are associated with known life are emphasized while the predominant chemical products that are not associated with life and would interfere with progress toward life are downplayed.

In the years following Miller's experiments, the atmospheric conditions of primitive Earth have been debated continuously—a predictable conundrum given the extreme low-confidence in any evidence from such a profoundly distant past. Bada presented his arguments that Miller's experimental conditions were appropriate but also conceded that "there remains considerable uncertainty regarding when, where and how the raw materials needed for prebiotic reactions and molecular evolution were produced" ([74], 2187).

In 2011, Dustin Trail and colleagues at Rensselaer Polytechnic Institute studied the oxidation state of cerium found in zircons that are thought to be as old as the Earth itself, even predating the known rock record [75]. They concluded that the oxidation state of the cerium was much higher than expected, suggesting that prebiotic synthesis should start with an entirely different set of gases: CO_2, H_2O, N_2, and SO_2. According to author Bruce Watson, "We can now say with some certainty that many scientists studying the origins of life on Earth simply picked the wrong atmosphere" [76]. Here, the subjective statement "some certainty" is an optimistic way to convey a lack of real confidence in the atmospheric gasses. Prebiotic synthesis experiments based on the more neutral atmosphere that Trail and colleagues suggested produce less diversity of amino acids and a lower yield than the reducing atmosphere that Miller used [77].

Others have attempted to sidestep the uncertainty over atmospheric conditions by focusing on aquatic conditions for prebiotic chemistry, but this too is mired in debate. The extreme temperature and acidity of "black smokers" and "white smokers," two types of hydrothermal vents on the ocean floor, have been proposed as sites for prebiotic chemistry [78]. Nick Lane, a biochemist at University College London, has argued that a very different, nonsmoking alkaline hydrothermal vent is the right environment for prebiotic chemistry [64].

With all of the debate over appropriate prebiotic conditions on Earth, some find the possibility of prebiotic chemistry in outer space to be more attractive [79, 80]. Indeed, some building blocks of life have been found in meteorites [81], and Saturn's moon Enceladus appears to have produced "complex macromolecular organic material with molecular masses above 200 atomic mass units" [82].

Thus, we have some evidence that at least some amino acids can be produced naturally in trace amounts, along with a large majority of interfering, unwanted products. However, we also have many hypothesized and debated conditions for prebiotic synthesis of amino acids, with very little confidence in the actual conditions that supposedly generated the first amino acids.

Phospholipids

Surviving a winter in Minnesota is nearly impossible unless one is surrounded by a "membrane" for maintaining a thermal gradient. The membrane (e.g., a coat, a building, or a car) serves to keep a small region warm while being surrounded by bitter cold. Similarly, life cannot exist without membranes to maintain chemical and electrical gradients[25] and to separate wanted from unwanted materials. In life, phospholipids are the foundation of membranes. Phospholipids consist of a phosphate group, a glycerol molecule, and fatty acids (Figure 7). The phosphate group likes to be in the presence of water, whereas the fatty acids are repelled by water. Phospholipids sometimes self-assemble into a bilayer in the presence of water. Here, two layers of phospholipids arrange themselves with the fatty acids together in the middle (where there is no water) and the phosphate groups at opposing ends, facing the water.

Determining how the first phospholipids could have formed via prebiotic synthesis is quite a challenge because bacteria and archaea have very different phospholipids[26] and because the enzymes that produce the glycerol phosphate in bacteria and archaea are quite different [83]. Despite these fundamental differences, current dogma is committed to a common ancestor for bacteria and archaea. This apparent contradiction has provoked a variety of creative theories to explain membrane evolution in bacteria and archaea [83]. Each theory comes with only a subjective argument

---

25. A chemical gradient is a higher concentration of a chemical in one region compared to another; an electrical gradient is a higher concentration of electric charge in one region compared to another (i.e., producing a voltage).
26. Bacteria have glycerol-3-phosphate with ester-linked fatty acids, while archaea have glycerol-1-phosphate with ether-linked isoprenoid chains.

because the paucity of available evidence cannot be used to confirm one theory over another. With no clear picture of which kind of phospholipids came first, it is very difficult to claim victory in attempts to derive the appropriate phospholipids via simulated prebiotic synthesis.

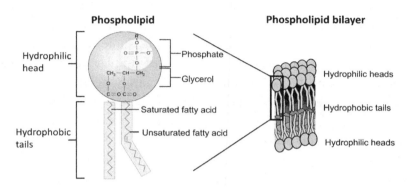

Figure 7. A schematic view of a phospholipid and a phospholipid bilayer. *Left:* The components of a single phospholipid. The hydrophilic regions have a strong affinity for water, whereas the hydrophobic regions are repulsed by water. *Right:* In water, phospholipids can spontaneously arrange into a bilayer that can form a vesicle.

In 1977, Hargreaves, Mulvihill, and Deamer conducted experiments to suggest that some phospholipids can form upon dehydration of an aqueous solution. Of the phosphorus in the reaction mixture, up to 0.2% reacted to form phospholipids. Upon partial purification via precipitation with acetone, the phospholipids were capable of self-assembly into vesicles [84]. Returning to our simplified mantra of "A+B produces C, under conditions D, E, and F," the phospholipid products that they produced (C) are not actually found in known life. Thus, a stretch of the imagination is required to believe that these experiments represent direct evidence for natural formation of the actual phospholipids of life.

Nevertheless, their work provided some hope that some phospho-lipids could have been produced, and may have formed vesicles, under a set of specific conditions.

For those who are interested, a slew of similar papers that also reported a variety of experimental conditions to produce combi-nations of lipid and phosphate are summarized in Table 3 of Fiore and Strazewski [85]. Recognizing the great challenges for prebi-otic production of the phospholipids of life, some suggest that the membranes of first life were composed of simpler molecules that contained opposing water-loving and lipid-loving ends (i.e., am-phiphilic molecules). Validating this hypothesis would require a prebiotic explanation for the arrival of these first membranes, fol-lowed by an explanation of how these membranes transitioned to the phospholipid membranes of all known life while maintaining membrane function. Fiore and Strazewski summarized the cur-rent state of prebiotic phospholipid chemistry as: "It is yet to be determined how the different lipid precursors formed abiotically to give more complex molecules like phospholipids" [85].

Thus, as with amino acids, we are left with low-confidence hints of possibilities, perhaps just enough evidence to encourage those who want to believe that prebiotic chemistry is the source of life.

Nucleotides

The fundamental building blocks of RNA or DNA include a ni-trogenous base (nucleobase) combined with a pentose sugar and a phosphate molecule. The proper combination of these three mol-ecules is a nucleotide (see Figure 8). The proper combination is easy to take for granted because students of biology are exposed to only this one arrangement—the arrangement found in all of life. In reality, a single phosphate group, a ribose, and a nucleobase can combine in hundreds of different ways.

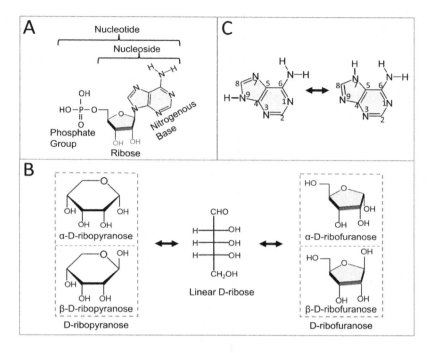

Figure 8. Many forms of nucleotides. *A*, nucleotide and its constituent parts. A nitrogenous base (adenine in this case) joined with a ribose sugar ring via a carbon-nitrogen bond constitutes a nucleoside. A nucleoside becomes a nucleotide when it is joined by one or more phosphate groups. *B*, Chemical equilibrium of D-ribose in water. D-ribose exists in five different forms in water. The ribopyranose forms on the left are the most stable; the linear form in the middle is the least stable. DNAs and RNAs only use the β-D-ribofuranose form of the lower right. Any of the four hydroxy (OH) groups can be used to join a phosphate group or a nucleobase in each of the five forms of ribose. *C*, Chemical equilibrium of adenine in water. Adenine can exist in two forms in water, providing three locations (N-7, N-9, and the exocyclic amino group) for bonding to ribose.

As a rudimentary example, consider the adenine ribonucleotide shown in Figure 8A. Ribose exists in five different forms in water solution (Figure 8B). Adenine could bond to any one of the four hydroxyl (OH) groups of ribose, and phosphate could bond with any of the three remaining hydroxyl groups. Adenine has a choice of three NH locations for bonding to ribose (Figure 8C). Thus, we have 5 X 4 X 3 X 3 = 180 possible arrangements of an adenine nucleotide, but only one (i.e., the canonical form) is observed in all of life. Similar possibilities exist for the other nucleotides. Of course, some arrangements are more energetically favorable than others, but that is beyond the scope of this simple example. Given a "soup" of nucleotides where only 1 out of 180 has the canonical arrangement, the probability of linking a chain to make an RNA of any reasonable length is effectively zero. For example, the chances of connecting a chain of forty canonical nucleotides in such a soup would be approximately one chance in ten followed by ninety zeros (10^{90}), which is far less likely than the chance of locating one specific atom in the entire universe. In reality, the situation is substantially worse because we have assumed a very limited molecular diversity for the "soup." We have only considered the combination of a single chirality of ribose with adenine and phosphate, not the extremely wide variety of other possible molecules, most of which are unrelated to life and would interfere with the formation of a proper chain.

The above discussion also assumes that prebiotic chemistry can produce the building blocks of nucleotides. Although supporting evidence is accumulating, that assumption cannot be taken for granted. Starting with the production of the pentose sugar, ribose is of greatest interest because RNA is thought to have preceded DNA in life, as part of the "RNA world" hypothesis [86]. The well-known formose reaction has been used to explain the prebiotic formation of ribose by polymerization of formaldehyde. However, ribose is a minor product of this reaction. As Springsteen and Joyce explained, "Ribose would have been only a small component of a highly complex mix of sugars resulting from the condensation of formaldehyde in a prebiotic world. In addition, ribose is more reactive and degrades more rapidly compared with most other monosaccharides" [87]. This has led many to question the feasibility of the RNA world hypothesis.

The most promising report of "prebiotic" synthesis of nucleotides was published in the journal *Science* in the fall of 2019 [88]. This report suggests that nucleosides could have formed via wet-dry cycles, given a long list of requirements: supplies of solid urea, ribose, and zinc metal; addition of borate to avoid incorrect reactions; precipitation of intermediate chemicals followed by washing away of reactants, followed by return of those reactants later in the process (specifically, the chemical 3-aminoisoxazole was essential for synthesis of some nucleosides but it inhibited synthesis of other nucleosides); and a correct sequence of wet and dry cycles at the right pH. After the nucleosides formed, they suggest that the addition of phosphate would have produced complete nucleotides in a prebiotic world. Despite this lengthy and complex list of required conditions, they claim that their approach to nucleotide synthesis is "prebiotically plausible"—a claim that is incredibly easy to make but incredibly difficult to support.

Back to the Forest

Even though the above foray into prebiotic chemistry was relatively brief, there is a risk of getting lost in the details. Prebiotic chemistry is replete with bold claims, but each experiment addresses only a small portion of abiogenesis in isolation, and each has many assumed conditions. Some zealots for abiogenesis find themselves satisfied with the meager evidence for prebiotic production of building blocks. For example, well before most of the publications that we just reviewed, George Gaylord Simpson, perhaps the best-known paleontologist of the twentieth century, said the following:

The consensus is that life did arise naturally from the nonliving and that even the first living things were not specially created. The conclusion has, indeed, really become inescapable, for the first steps in that process have already been repeated in several laboratories [27].

The Stairway to Life (Figure 6) provides a decidedly sobering perspective of reality. Thus far, we have only progressed through a portion of the first step (out of twelve steps), and all of the prebiotic synthesis described occurred under debatable prebiotic conditions. These assumed prebiotic conditions cannot be validated because the available evidence relating to the actual conditions of prebiotic synthesis is extraordinarily weak.

Following the prebiotic synthesis of these building blocks, completion of the first step of the Stairway to Life would require: 1) avoiding degradation, 2) separating the desired components, filtering out the undesired components from a very complex mixture, and 3) concentrating the building blocks (only the desired building blocks) in one location.

Avoiding Degradation

Hundreds of millions of years of "deep time" is frequently cited as the saving feature for the profound improbability of each step of the Stairway. Yet time is only an ally of a slow construction process if degradation is ignored. As a useful analogy, imagine the very slow construction of a house. The earthmovers clear the site and dig a foundation. The masons arrive one thousand years later and find a dense forest with a slight depression in one area. Nevertheless, they do their best to lay the foundation. After another thousand years, the carpenters arrive and find a dense forest and sparse remnants of cement and cinder block. Undaunted, they construct the wooden frame of a house. The roofers arrive a thousand years later to find a dense forest and almost no detectable remnant of any prior construction effort. Clearly, a house can never be constructed in such a manner.

For abiogenesis, the situation is far worse. Here, the process of ascending the twelve steps of Figure 6 is thought to have occurred over hundreds of millions of years. The sources of energy that are thought to be needed for construction of larger and more complex molecules (i.e., thermal, radiation, ultraviolet light, electricity, etc.) are all quite capable of breaking larger molecules into smaller molecules. The thermodynamic drive to increase entropy can only be overcome by the continuous infusion of energy combined with the proper "engine" to convert the energy into a building process rather than a destructive process.

Separation

All the reactions designed to synthesize the building blocks produce complex mixtures of a variety of molecules, "intractable mixtures" [89] or "asphalts" [90], which contain mostly unwanted materials. Life is based upon a specific set of phospholipids, twenty amino acids, and five nucleobases, yet thousands of other possible configurations would be produced by the same prebiotic conditions. For example, the highly touted Murchison meteorite, rich in organic contents, contains "tens of thousands of different molecular compositions, and likely millions of diverse structures," which "suggests that the extraterrestrial chemodiversity is high compared to terrestrial relevant biological- and biogeochemical-driven chemical space" [81]. Knowing that the vast majority of abiotically produced molecules are undesirable and expecting constructive interactions between only the rare desired molecules contradicts reality. Although laboratory synthesis run by human intellect can work with pure reagents, a method is needed for the required prebiotic separation of the desired molecules. Synthetic biologist Steven Benner summarizes the challenge:

> Chemical theories, including the second law of thermodynamics, bonding theory that describes the "space" accessible to sets of atoms, and structure theory requiring that replication systems occupy only tiny fractions of that space, suggest that it is impossible for *any* non-living chemical system to escape devolution to enter into the Darwinian world of the "living" [90]. [original emphasis]

Concentration

Even if the desired building blocks could somehow be separated from the undesired components, the necessary interactions between the building blocks would require a natural means for concentration. Building blocks drifting about randomly in an ocean, a lake, or a pond would not achieve sufficient concentration to interact, except by way of evaporation or freezing. Nick Lane questions this approach to concentration:

> Either freezing or evaporating to dryness could potentially increase the concentration of organics, but these are drastic methods, hardly congruent with the physically stable state that is the defining feature of all living cells ([64], 93).

Lane prefers to envision concentration occurring inside the porous walls of alkaline hydrothermal vents at the bottom of the ocean. However, the individual pores in the walls of the vents are highly unlikely to remain stable over the expected time course (millions of years) for abiogenesis.

To summarize this chapter, a prebiotic solution to the first step in the Stairway to Life has received a great deal of attention in the last sixty years but is far from complete. Some hints of encouraging results have been obtained in controlled laboratory environments, but these experiments are built upon layers of assumptions about prebiotic Earth—assumptions that cannot be validated—and require pure reagents and careful supervision by intelligent agents (i.e., scientists). As we will see, such hints of encouragement are increasingly rare as we climb the remaining eleven steps.

Chapter 8
Homochirality of Building Blocks

I n 1957, the German pharmaceutical company Chemie Grünenthal began marketing the drug thalidomide. Initially used as a sedative, the drug was later recognized as a very successful treatment for morning sickness during pregnancy. Thousands of pregnant women in West Germany, the UK, Australia, and Canada enjoyed the temporary benefits of the drug. However, within a few years of market release, reports of severe birth defects began to surface. The most prominent defect was phocomelia—severe malformation of the limbs. By the early 1960s, the drug was banned in many countries, having been clearly associated with severe birth defects in about ten thousand children.

Thalidomide exists in two chiral forms (Figure 9). The process to produce thalidomide resulted in equal portions of the two forms (such a mixture is called a racemic mixture). One form behaves as a powerful sedative, and the other form causes severe birth defects [91]. The saga of thalidomide carries a powerful lesson: the spatial orientation of a molecule can be as powerful as its constituents. Chirality may seem like a minor issue, but it can have profound impact on molecular function, and life is exquisitely sensitive to chirality.

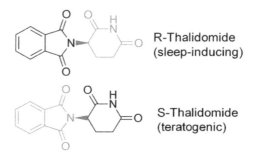

R-Thalidomide
(sleep-inducing)

S-Thalidomide
(teratogenic)

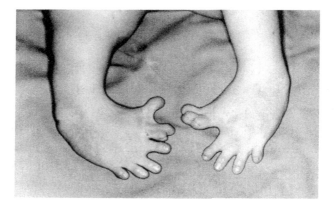

Figure 9. Chirality and effects of thalidomide. *Top:* The two chiral forms of thalidomide. The R-form, which acts as a sedative, has the central nitrogen rising above the plane of this page. The S-form, which causes malformation of embryos (i.e., it is teratogenic), has the central nitrogen below the plane of this page. *Bottom:* An example of the effects of thalidomide.

Although it took a disaster like thalidomide to raise awareness of chirality in the development of pharmaceuticals, life has always had a deep appreciation for the importance of chirality. Living organisms frequently exhibit an absolute discrimination of chirality, tolerating molecules with only a single chiral form, also known as homochirality. Homochirality is a distinguishing characteristic of living organisms [92]. As mentioned in Chapter 2, carbons 1', 3', and 4' of the deoxyribose rings in DNA are chiral locations (also known as stereocenters). DNA could therefore exist in a very wide variety of possible chiral configurations, but all life makes use of the exact same configuration. RNA also has the same chirality in every known form of life, even though each RNA nucleotide has one additional stereocenter when compared to DNA (carbon 2').[27] The production of RNA via polymerization of ribonucleotides is known to be inhibited by the presence of ribonucleotides with the wrong chirality [93]. Therefore, a natural means of filtering out undesired chirality would have to precede any polymerization of ribonucleotides to make homochiral RNA.

Amino acids in living organisms are almost exclusively left-handed.[28] Incorrect chirality in just one amino acid of a protein can interfere with function: "If only one amino acid is replaced by its optical (chiral) counterpart the formed protein will not fulfill its tasks properly because of destabilization effects induced by the distorted structure of α-helices and β-sheets" [95]. Therefore, a natural means of filtering out undesired chirality in amino acids is required before the first polymerization of amino acids into proteins.

Cell membranes are also homochiral in all of life. The glycerol molecule of every phospholipid is exclusively left-handed in bacteria and eukaryotes. Unexplainably, the same glycerol molecule is exclusively right-handed in archaea. Incidentally, the enzymes responsible for the production of these left-handed and right-handed

---

27. For completeness, each DNA nucleotide (i.e., a deoxyribonucleotide) has three stereocenters and each RNA nucleotide (i.e., a ribonucleotide) has four stereocenters, with each stereocenter capable of existing in either chiral form. Yet all of life has the same chirality at each stereocenter. The complex chirality of these molecules is frequently simplified, referring to them as "right-handed" in all of life.

28. For very rare exceptions, see Konno et al. [94].

forms of glycerol are composed exclusively of left-handed amino acids, although distinctly different sequences of amino acids comprise the enzymes of bacteria and archaea ([96], 149).

Homochirality is so unique to living organisms, and so unnatural outside of living organisms, that tests of homochirality have been applied to amino acids of unknown sources to determine if they were formed by abiotic reactions (i.e., not homochiral) or produced by living organisms (i.e., homochiral). In other words, if you happen to stumble upon a sample of amino acids and you observe homochirality, you can be assured that they were produced by living organisms, not an abiotic process [97].

Although the amino acids in proteins are homochiral, each chiral amino acid has a small probability of randomly switching its chirality over time. Thus, living organisms must constantly replace proteins as they degrade. After death, the amino acids naturally decay to a racemic mixture because they are no longer replaced. This property has been proposed as a means to estimate ages in archeology and paleobiology [98].

How did life become so discriminatory in its chirality? Laboratory efforts to synthesize compounds that favor one kind of chirality (referred to as enantioselective synthesis) must either begin with source materials that have a predominant chirality or make use of a catalyst that is homochiral. In all living systems, homochirality is produced and maintained by enzymes, which are themselves composed of homochiral amino acids that were specified through homochiral DNA and produced via homochiral messenger RNA, homochiral ribosomal RNA, and homochiral transfer RNA. No one has ever found a plausible abiotic explanation for how life could have become exclusively homochiral. This is but a brief description of the homochirality paradox of life, a great challenge for all who support abiogenesis.

Some who seek to encourage belief in abiogenesis find it convenient to avoid discussion of homochirality. The popular biology textbook *Biological Science* goes to great efforts to convince students that "life began when chemical evolution led to the production of a molecule that could promote its own replication" ([10], 57), yet chirality is never mentioned in its 1,418 pages. Biochemist Nick Lane wrote a 290-page book on abiogenesis called *The Vital Question* [64]. The book contains great detail on the chemistry of life and his theories on how chemistry transitioned to biology, yet the word "chirality" never graces a single page. Franklin Harold's *In Search of Cell History* begins with the assumption that life began naturally and walks the reader through hundreds of pages of hypothesized pathways, yet it never mentions chirality [99]. Well-known atheist Richard Dawkins has written and presented extensively on abiogenesis, yet his books do not broach the topic of chirality, and the internet only knows of Richard Dawkins referring to chirality when describing his rationale for wearing odd socks (because unlike shoes, socks generally lack chirality).

Others who seek to encourage belief in abiogenesis and are bold enough to acknowledge the paradox of homochirality refer to studies (summarized below) that suggest natural approaches to favoring one form of chirality. Those who are eager to dismiss concerns over the paradox of homochirality apparently find satisfaction in these results.

Louis Pasteur was the first person to separate a racemic mixture to produce a homochiral product. Tartaric acid, found in the sediments of fermenting wine, was known at the time to have chirality. Pasteur noted that under certain conditions, tartaric acid formed a mixture of two types of crystals. With painstaking manual separation of the two types of crystals (under a microscope with the use of tweezers), Pasteur was able to produce homochiral tartaric acid. Of the twenty amino acids that are common in living organisms, nineteen are chiral (glycine is not), but only two can form homochiral crystals like tartaric acid [92]. Thus, Pasteur's method not only required physical separation by an intelligent agent, but it would also only be possible for two of life's amino acids.

In 1995, the Japanese chemist Kenso Soai reported the first abiotic reaction that could increase the prevalence of one form of chirality in a mixture, given a starting excess of one form of chirality [100]. This reaction is accelerated by the product of the reaction (i.e., it is an autocatalytic reaction). Starting with only 0.1% excess of one form of chirality over the other, this reaction has led to up to 85% of one chiral form and 15% of the other. Although 85% excess of one form of chirality in a mixture may seem impressive, the probability of randomly forming any homochiral protein with 1,100 amino acids under these conditions approximates the chance of finding one specific atom in the known universe. Also, the Soai reaction does not fit within the expected conditions on the prebiotic Earth. As noted by Donna Blackmond, an origin-of-life research chemist at the Scripps Institute, "The experimental conditions of the Soai reaction preclude it from being of direct prebiotic importance, because it is unlikely that the dialkylzinc chemistry involved would thrive in an aqueous, aerobic prebiotic environment" [92].

Another approach to obtain a chiral excess, called chiral amnesia, could possibly apply to only two specific amino acids [101]. A third technique known as crystal engineering phase behavior requires an excess of one form of chirality at the outset and pure amino acids dissolved into a solvent. The solvent and amino acids then form together into a crystal structure, leaving an excess of chirality in the remaining solution [102]. In a fourth approach, mineral surfaces like quartz and calcite can demonstrate some minor preferences for one chirality of amino acids. However, the minerals must be free from any impurities, can only generate chiral excess in the range of about 10%, and can perform this function only over microscopic ranges of the crystals [103, 104].

Finally, a paper from 2019 suggests that rotary stirring and evaporation of a solution of larger molecules can produce chiral supermolecules. The individual molecules in the solution were not chiral, but upon rotary stirring and evaporation, the individual molecules aggregated (i.e., remained individual molecules but formed associations with neighboring molecules) to produce a chiral solid. The chirality, which depended on the rotation direction, was lost when the solid was subsequently dissolved. This is like taking individual stairsteps (which are not chiral), placing them in a swimming pool, stirring the water to create a vortex, then evaporating the water to produce a spiral staircase that twists according to the direction of the vortex. This is an interesting finding, but it doesn't explain how to produce homochiral molecules like amino acids or sugars. Nevertheless, the authors summarize their work with a hope that their technique will provide "a clue to the origin of the homochirality of life" [105].

In summary, known techniques to achieve chiral excess in the absence of components from living organisms fall far short of solving the homochirality paradox of life. The above discussion focused predominantly on the chirality of amino acids; the complex homochirality of nucleotides and the different forms of homochiral phospholipids for archaea versus bacteria and eukaryotes further compound the homochirality paradox of life. Finally, those who support abiogenesis must also provide a means to overcome the natural random switching of chirality over time—a means for somehow maintaining chiral purity over the great spans of time that are expected for abiogenesis. The second step on the Stairway to Life thus appears to be a greater challenge than the first.

Chapter 9

A Solution for the Water Paradox

Organic synthesis is very hard to do in water. Highly oxygenated organic compounds are needed. The synthetic chemist must project the oxygenated groups out toward the water domain, and project the non-oxygenated groups in toward each other, thus generating a hydrophobic domain. It is very hard to do.

—James Tour [106]

Now working under the (unsupported) assumptions that the basic building blocks were formed abiotically, that the desired building blocks were selected out of a pool of random undesired molecules and concentrated in one location, and that an abiotic means of achieving homochirality existed, we next need a means of properly linking together, or polymerizing, the building blocks. We previously discussed the three requirements for prebiotic synthesis from Leslie Orgel, where two of the three criteria were easily met by the subjective interpretation of the investigator. The one objective requirement was: "Reactions must occur in water or in the absence of a solvent" [70]. Recognizing that polymerization is extremely constrained in the absence of a solvent, scientists have focused on the polymerization of biomolecules in water.

Water is essential for all known life. Water and life are so intimately connected that they are almost synonymous; the mere suggestion of discovering water on another planet is commonly followed by a suggestion that there could be life. However, organic synthesis is highly constrained in water: water discourages the polymerization of nucleotides to make DNA or RNA; water discourages the polymerization of amino acids to make proteins; and water naturally degrades DNA, RNA, and proteins. This creates the "paradox of water," because water is both essential to life and detrimental to the start of life.

The polymerization reactions that produce DNA or RNA from nucleotides, as well as those that produce proteins from amino acids, each produce one molecule of water for each added monomer. Therefore, the presence of water as a solvent naturally drives these reactions in the wrong direction. Nick Lane describes this as "a bit like trying to wring out a wet cloth under water" ([64], 98). In life, this polymerization reaction must be driven by a source of energy, just as your car needs a source of energy to move uphill.

A recent report claimed a major advancement toward prebiotic production of proteins in water [107]. However, the production of peptide bonds in water requires ferricyanide and hydrogen sulfide to be stored separately and added separately in sequential steps. In other words, ferricyanide must be added, then washed away, then hydrogen sulfide must be added, then washed away, and this precise sequence must be repeated for each additional amino acid. The ferricyanide and hydrogen sulfide cannot be added at the same time because they are highly reactive with each other. Also, the experiment started with pure, homochiral, activated amino acids. These conditions are well suited for peptide synthesis in a controlled laboratory, but they are hardly realistic in a prebiotic world.

In the formation of DNA, the bonds between nitrogenous bases (i.e., guanine paired with cytosine and adenine paired with thymine) are essential to maintain the double-helix structure. However, in the presence of water, these bonds do not form between free nitrogenous bases, nor do they form between nitrogenous bases contained in free nucleosides or nucleotides. Rather than forming the necessary hydrogen bonds between nitrogenous bases, the bases form hydrogen bonds with water [108, 109]. In life, amino acids and nucleotides are linked via a reaction that requires energy from adenosine triphosphate (ATP). Along with providing energy, the conversion of ATP to adenosine diphosphate (ADP) absorbs one water molecule, which facilitates the polymerization reaction. In life, the ATP is commonly produced by a complex process of transferring electrons from carbon (food) sources to oxygen (see Chapter 16). In a prebiotic world, some other means of overcoming the paradox of water is necessary.

Water not only inhibits the polymerization of DNA and RNA, but it also corrodes existing DNA and RNA, requiring life-forms to maintain complex molecular mechanisms to repair or replace biopolymers. The presence of water can result in deamination and depurination. In deamination, a cytosine nucleobase of DNA is converted to uracil, thus the normal cytosine–guanine base pairing could be mutated to form a uracil–adenine base pair. Deamination also converts adenine to hypoxanthine. Rather than form the expected adenine–thymine base pair, unrepaired hypoxanthine pairs with cytosine.

Water also damages DNA via depurination, where adenine or guanine is released from their deoxyribose sugar, leaving what is called an "abasic site" in the DNA. In a typical human cell, it has been estimated that 2,000-10,000 depurinations occur each day [110, 111], and depurination is known to play a role in cancer formation [112]. Hydrolytic depurination is a major form of damage to DNA postmortem or ex vivo because the repair mechanisms are no longer active [110].

Chapter 14 will further explain how the damage inflicted by water leads to an essential requirement for molecular repair mechanisms to maintain biopolymers. Yet again we see that natural processes inherently degrade—not provide—components of life. Living organisms must actively work to prevent or correct degradative natural processes.

The paradox of water has led to fantastical theories, such as the formation of prebiotic molecules and the start of life in an environment where formamide is the solvent and later having life adapt to water as a solvent (even though the natural production of formamide is exceedingly rare on the Earth and formamide is quite toxic to existing life-forms) [113].

The paradox of water appears to be insurmountable for abiogenesis. Those who maintain support for abiogenesis are left to choose among few options: ignoring the issue, expecting the prebiotic world to supply the type of controlled and purified conditions of an organic synthesis laboratory, proposing a hypothetical "proto-solvent" for life, or hoping that someone else will solve the paradox.

Chapter 10

Consistent Linkage of Building Blocks

In living organisms, RNA, DNA, and proteins are chains of monomers that are linked together with perfect consistency, like boxcars perfectly aligned on the tracks and interconnected to form a long train. This "homolinkage" of long biopolymers is very difficult to achieve abiotically, even in modern laboratories run by human intellect. Abiotic chemical reactions to link chains of monomers end up looking more like a train derailment unless complex and highly controlled chemical reactions are employed to connect each monomer correctly (like the oligonucleotide synthesis described in Chapter 2, which still had a significant likelihood of error). We reviewed the difficulties of obtaining the "proper" form of nucleotides and amino acids in Chapter 7, appreciating that the desired forms of nucleotides and amino acids are an extreme rarity. In this chapter, we assume that the individual nucleotides (based on ribose or deoxyribose) and amino acids could have been produced abiotically, the proper forms could somehow be separated from the vast majority of incorrect forms, and the proper forms could somehow be concentrated in one location. We also now assume that abiotic solutions exist for the paradox of homochirality and the paradox of water. The next challenge is an abiotic mechanism to achieve consistent linkage of the nucleotides and amino acids to form long biopolymers.

Homolinkage of Nucleic Acids

Every biology and genetics textbook contains a diagram of DNA's molecular structure. These diagrams always depict nucleotides arranged in a consistent manner along the length of the double helix. The general structure of DNA and RNA is familiar because all life is based upon the same molecular arrangement. This all-too-familiar arrangement can lead to the incorrect assumption that it is the only possible arrangement—an arrangement that is so energetically favored that it has no rival.

The modern laboratory technique for oligonucleotide synthesis, as described in Chapter 2, is clearly too complex and unnatural for consideration in a prebiotic world. Other "more prebiotic" approaches to DNA or RNA synthesis have been attempted for at least the last twenty years. To dramatically simplify the goal of producing the molecular arrangement found in all of life, these experiments all began with pure homochiral nucleotides. All that remained was the final step of polymerizing the pure nucleotide monomers into a linear chain via the proper bonds (3', 5' phosphodiester bonds as shown in Figure 10A, not improper bonds like the example of Figure 10D). Chapter 9 discussed the difficulty of achieving this polymerization step abiotically in water. To overcome this limitation, the investigators started with unnaturally activated nucleotides (i.e., nucleotides that were modified to be more reactive but are therefore less stable), usually 5'-phosphorimidazolides.

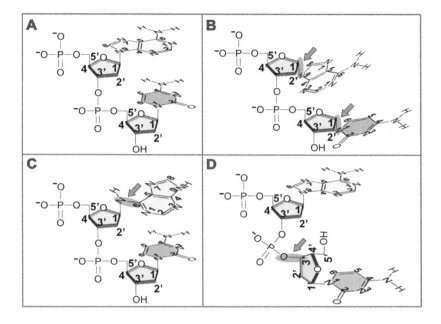

Figure 10. A few of the possible molecular structures for an adenine cytosine deoxyribose dinucleotide. The version in *A* is common to DNA in all known life. The *B, C,* and *D* versions are not found in living organisms. Chemical bonds in *B, C,* and *D* that are different from those in *A* are shaded and highlighted with arrows.

In the early 1990s, under prescribed conditions including proper concentration, temperature, pH, and appropriate catalysts, Ferris and Ertem demonstrated the formation of dinucleotides (i.e., the connection of two nucleotides) and trace amounts of longer polymers [114]. The longest observed chain contained eleven monomers, with a yield of 0.0003. However, one-third of the phosphodiester bonds were incorrect. In more recent experiments, the longest chains (up to fifty monomers) and the highest production of molecules with the correct bonds have been achieved in the presence of montmorillonite clay [115–118]. With purine nucleotides (adenosine and guanine), the percentage of correct phosphodiester bonds actually exceeded that of the incorrect bonds. However, the addition of each monomer to the chain comes with a probability of incorrect bonding, and one incorrect bond irreversibly destroys the homolinkage of the growing polymer, just as a train with one derailed boxcar can destroy the entire train. Therefore, the synthetic yield of biopolymers with the desired homolinkage decreases exponentially as the length of the biopolymer increases—even when starting only with pure building blocks. Also, in the presence of montmorillonite, polymerization of purine nucleotides (i.e., adenine and guanine) is favored over pyrimidine nucleotides (i.e., cytosine, thymine, and uracil) [118–120]. This would constrain the potential information-carrying capacity of the resulting polymers, somewhat like requiring an author to have the letters A through M appear in their writing twice as often as the letters N through Z.

Another issue with the montmorillonite-catalyzed reaction is that the most successful polymerization occurred with an inosine nitrogenous base, which is not used to synthesize natural DNA or RNA [121]. Also, the resulting oligomers decompose in the presence of water (as discussed in Chapter 9), and the clay accelerates this decomposition. Finally, for the longer polymers, intramolecular cyclization (i.e., irreversible bonding of one end of the growing molecule to its other end to create a cyclical polymer that can no longer grow) also becomes a major obstacle to polymerization [122].

A more recent development is to synthesize oligonucleotides under dehydrating conditions—i.e., using essentially dry materials [123–128]. These reactions, under very specific conditions, can produce oligomers in the range of twenty monomers in length. This research group, led by Professor Ernesto Di Mauro, strongly advocates for "molecular Darwinism" and a one-pot proton-irradiated reaction to generate all the basic building blocks of life. However, it is remarkable that they never start their oligo-merization reactions with the complex mixture of products generated in their one-pot reactions. Rather, they start over with highly purified nucleotides [124–129] because they are fully aware of the problem of the "asphalt paradox," which states that an "enormous amount of empirical data have established, as a rule, that organic systems, given energy and left to themselves, devolve to give use-lessly complex mixtures, 'asphalts'" [90]. In Professor Di Mauro and his colleagues' own words, "As Benner noted, prebiotic chem-istry without selection leads to tar formation" [129].

Thus, under the most favorable conditions, abiotic homolink-age of approximately one hundred nucleotides can be achieved with very low yield and several limitations. Production of DNA with perfect homolinkage throughout the length of a genome (for example, there are approximately 500,000 nucleotides in the sim-plest known free-living organism's genome) is impossible without the molecular machinery that is available only in living organisms.

Homolinkage of Amino Acids

Every biology textbook also contains a diagram of the common structure of proteins, showing a chain of amino acids joined con-sistently via α-peptide bonds. This provides the false impression that amino acids can only join via α-peptide bonds to form pro-teins, as they do in living organisms when ribosomes are control-ling the reactions. In reality, the side chain of an α-amino acid can interact with the side chain, the α-amino group, or the α-carboxyl group of another amino acid to form nonpeptide bonds or non-α-peptide bonds. Figure 11 shows some of the potential products when two amino acids (a lysine and a glutamic acid) combine. The two are joined via the expected α-peptide bonds in panels A and B, and by alternate bonds in panels C through G. As with DNA and

RNA, the probability of achieving homolinkage in a polypeptide decreases exponentially with increasing molecular size.

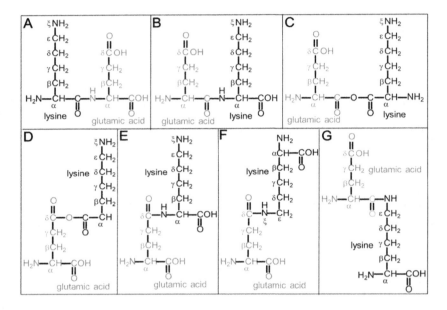

Figure 11. Some potential reaction products of a lysine and a glutamic acid (gray). In *A* and *B*, a lysine and a glutamic acid joined by a normal α-peptide bond. In *C* and *D*, a lysine and a glutamic acid joined by an ester bond. In *E* through *G*, a lysine and a glutamic acid joined by non-α-peptide bonds.

The challenge of producing consistent α-peptide bonds was demonstrated by the very experiment that Sidney Fox and colleagues performed in an effort to show that life could have originated from amino acids by natural means. They heated a mixture of pure amino acids and named their products proteinoids, implying that the products are related to proteins. Ironically, their experiment did not produce proteins in which the amino acids are lined up like boxcars to produce a long train. Instead, their experiment produced more of a train wreck, where the majority of bonds were not the desired α-peptide bond [130, 131].

The most recent and most promising approach to prebiotic homolinkage of amino acids was described in Chapter 9 [107]. This method works even in the presence of water but requires sequential (not simultaneous) delivery of two reagents (hydrogen sulfide and ferricyanide) for each added amino acid.

Even with modern laboratory technology to synthesize polypeptides without the use of cells, DNA, or enzymes (via a process known as solid-phase peptide synthesis), unwanted reactions (i.e., reactions without homolinkage) are common, and each added amino acid takes more than one minute of reaction time [132]. Successful synthesis of small proteins (on the order of one hundred amino acids) in less than twenty-four hours is considered to be a major accomplishment in the modern era [133]. For comparison, protein synthesis in the ribosomes of *E. coli* occurs at the rate of approximately 1,200 amino acids per minute with unquestionably superior accuracy. The great difficulty in producing polypeptides, even with high-purity homochiral reagents and highly constrained reaction conditions, provides a sobering perspective on the possibilities of abiotic synthesis of useful proteins.

All empirical evidence tells us that homolinkage of DNA, RNA, and proteins can only be achieved via the highly specific and catalytic activity of enzymes and ribozymes[29] or via the careful planning of intelligent agents. In short, without the intervention of intelligent agents, existing biopolymers are required for the production of biopolymers.

---

29. Whereas enzymes are proteins that facilitate biochemical and metabolic reactions, ribozymes are RNA molecules that facilitate biochemical and metabolic reactions.

Chapter 11

Biopolymer Reproduction

A universally accepted definition of life, one that clearly distinguishes "living" from "nonliving," remains elusive. However, reproduction is generally seen as a fundamental axiom of life. At some point in the hypothetical advancement from chemistry to biology, the ability to reproduce would have to emerge. All known cells come from other cells, but the process of cellular reproduction is far too complex a starting point. Abiogenesis must build from the most basic processes and explain how complexity can accumulate by purely natural means. If abiogenesis has any merit, reproduction must have occurred long before the arrival of the first living cell; reproduction must have started at the molecular level.[30]

---

30. Origin-of-life researchers are sometimes organized into two major camps: replication-first and metabolism-first. By placing this chapter before the discussion of energy harnessing (Chapter 16), this book arguably takes a replication-first stance. However, the ordering of the Stairway to Life is not our focus. The challenges posed by each step must be overcome for abiogenesis to occur. Reordering the steps does not reduce the total challenge. In a metabolism-first scenario, even if an adequate source of energy is available to develop replicating molecules, the challenges posed in this chapter will remain.

As with each chapter in Part II, we begin this discussion of self-replicating molecules by assuming that the challenges of all prior chapters have been overcome. Thus, we will set aside all concerns about the production of the monomers (ribonucleotides), chirality, the paradox of water, and homolinkage.

All uncontested living organisms reproduce DNA, and nearly all introductory biology textbooks claim that errors in DNA reproduction provide the raw materials for the Darwinian accumulation of complexity. However, reproduction of DNA is a very complex process; even the simplest prokaryotes require the coordination of at least fourteen enzymes (including twenty-five polypeptides) to reproduce DNA [134]. It would thus seem that DNA is a poor candidate for the first reproduced molecule.

RNA is also universal in life and is capable of storing information. Reproduction of RNA would thus allow for the dissemination of information. Any errors in the reproduction of RNA could provide raw material for the accumulation of complexity through natural selection. Natural selection of self-replicating molecules, like natural selection of reproducing organisms, could involve domination of the most successful replicators, the molecules that are most robust to environmental challenges, or perhaps those molecules with the ability to eliminate rivals (such as an ability to break bonds in rival molecules). We can thus imagine that a Darwinian-type evolution could be applied on a molecular scale, such that chemical evolution improves the function of self-replicating molecules over time.

The "RNA World" Hypothesis

In 1962, MIT Professor of Physics Alexander Rich combined these concepts to propose that RNA could have been central to the start of life [135]. In 1986, Walter Gilbert first called this the "RNA world" hypothesis of abiogenesis [86]. Sidney Altman and Thomas

Cech provided great encouragement for the RNA world hypothesis by demonstrating that RNA can also have enzymatic properties in the form of ribozymes. They received the Nobel prize for their efforts in 1989. Ribozymes are now known to be a fundamental component of ribosomes, which are responsible for the synthesis of proteins from messenger RNA. Thus, RNA can not only serve as the genotype (the information storage), but it can also serve as the phenotype (the function). RNA was beginning to look like the "jack-of-all-trades" molecule, a perfect candidate for the start of life. Leslie Orgel, a strong advocate for abiogenesis, wrote, "The demonstration that ribosomal peptide synthesis is a ribozyme-catalyzed reaction makes it almost certain that there was once an RNA world" [70]. This quote exposes the thinking of those in support of the RNA world hypothesis, although the claim that it is "almost certain" is certainly in need of a reality check. Efforts then focused on identifying self-replicating RNA molecules, one of the missing pieces in the RNA world hypothesis.

Spiegelman Creates a Monster

In the late 1960s, Sol Spiegelman generated great enthusiasm for the concept of self-replicating RNA. Based upon the behavior of RNA viruses that replicate their RNA inside cells, Spiegelman demonstrated that RNA from a bacterial virus (specifically, a Qβ bacteriophage containing about 4,200 nucleotides) could be reproduced outside of living organisms in a solution containing individual ribonucleotide building blocks. RNA is a single strand of ribonucleotides. Individual ribonucleotides in a solution have natural affinity for complementary pairing with RNA (e.g., ribonucleotides of guanine prefer to pair with cytosine on RNA, and ribonucleotides of adenine prefer to pair with uracil on RNA). Thinking of the RNA molecule as a template, the complementary

RNA monomers (ribonucleotides) could spontaneously align with the RNA template.

As a loosely related analogy, imagine that the RNA molecule is a long strip of individual magnets. Some of the magnets in the strip have their north pole exposed, and some have their south pole exposed. Thus, the strip of magnets contains a specific sequence of north and south polarities, which is a type of code or information storage (like a magnetic tape). When this strip is placed into a solution of free-floating magnets (RNA monomers), the free magnets will naturally attach to the strip: north poles of the free magnets will attach to the exposed south poles on the strip and vice versa. Now, if the free-floating magnets that attached to the strip were then bonded to each other to produce a second strip, the second strip would be complementary to the first strip (i.e., containing the opposite sequence of codes).

Similarly, if chemical bonds were formed between the RNA monomers that attached to the RNA molecule, a complementary RNA molecule would result, and a second round of this process would produce the complement of the complement, or a copy of the original RNA. The copies contain occasional errors, which could lead to improvement of the process. Spiegelman's paper came with a very provocative title: "An extracellular Darwinian experiment with a self-duplicating nucleic acid molecule," seemingly implying that self-replication and chemical evolution had already been demonstrated [136]. The authors reported that an RNA molecule "evolved" through seventy-five "generations" of self-replication in the lab, to arrive at an RNA molecule (known as "Spiegelman's Monster") that could replicate fifteen times faster than the original. The reader is led to believe that biopolymer reproduction and complexification (i.e., "chemical evolution") is no longer a concern for abiogenesis. To this day, authors like Addy Pross, in his book *What is Life?*, find great encouragement for abiogenesis from these results, concluding that "molecular self-replication reaction is a reality, a reaction that actually does take place, and most importantly, is autocatalytic" ([66], 68). Addy Pross goes on to base his entire argument for abiogenesis on the evolution of self-replicating molecules.

Unfortunately, a few inconvenient details of the work were neglected in making these claims. The replication of RNA not only required a supply of pure homochiral nucleotides, it also required a supply of Qβ replicase, a protein enzyme that was actually responsible for combining the nucleotides into RNA molecules. Qβ replicase is quite selective about the RNA that it will reproduce. An abiotic origin for Qβ replicase is absurd because it consists of a combination of four protein subunits and more than 1,200 amino acids in a specific sequence—an enzyme of great complexity [137]. Classifying the RNA as "self-replicating" required this essential ingredient to be dismissed. This is like claiming that computer viruses replicate themselves, forgetting that the computer hardware is an essential contributor to the process. Also unfortunately, the reported "evolution" of the RNA molecule over seventy-five generations to yield a substantially faster-reproducing RNA was actually a clear example of devolution. Compared to the original RNA molecule, the highly evolved Spiegelman's Monster was 83% smaller. Shorter RNAs will naturally be produced faster than longer RNAs. So in a type of parasitic devolution, shorter RNAs will be reproduced faster and will dominate the population of RNA molecules in a solution. This is sometimes called the "Spiegelman problem," and it is a fundamental limitation of any uncontrolled process of RNA replication. Indeed, the Qβ RNA began with four functional genes and ended up with 83% loss of information— hardly a poster child for evolution and the "complexification" required for abiogenesis. Other approaches to chemical evolution have yielded similar results: the smaller the molecule, the faster the replication [138].

Fertility Clinic for RNA

How can we get RNA to reproduce itself? Realization of the RNA world hypothesis would require replication of RNA from RNA alone, without the help of protein enzymes. One approach could involve one RNA molecule serving as a template, to which complementary RNA monomers would bind, and another RNA molecule serving as a "ribozyme" (an RNA with the ability to bond the aligned RNA monomers to each other) to produce a complement—not a copy—of the original RNA template. If the template molecule happened to be the same RNA sequence as the ribozyme, the ribozyme and template would be working together toward making more copies of themselves. In the above analogy of the magnetic strips, magnetic attraction would keep the second (complementary) strip of magnets strongly bonded to the first strip, which would inhibit subsequent rounds of copying. The strength of the bonding between the two strips would be proportional to the length of the strips. Unfortunately, this also occurs with RNA—the newly produced complementary version of the template (an "antisense RNA") has a tendency to remain bonded ("annealed") to the template RNA, making the combined molecule relatively useless.[31] The strength of this bonding is proportional to the length of the RNA. Although it is possible for shorter strands of annealed RNA (less than thirty base pairs) to separate at high temperatures, an RNA of less than thirty base pairs carries very little information, and two separated complementary strands of RNA are very likely

---

31. Living organisms sometimes produce antisense RNA, and some medical treatments apply antisense RNA to interfere with protein production by annealing with messenger RNA. In living organisms, but not in a prebiotic world, the enzyme ribonuclease H has the job of destroying annealed RNA such as this.

to find each other and reanneal before another round of copying can occur.

Because RNA self-replication must first generate a complementary RNA, the process naturally interferes with itself. In living cells, complex enzymes like Qβ replicase are able to keep the complementary RNA strands separated during replication. A proposed abiotic solution to this problem involved the addition of short peptides to the mixture to interfere with the annealing of complementary RNAs [139]. Unfortunately, the authors subsequently retracted the paper because the results could not be reproduced [140]. Speaking hypothetically, if the complementary RNA strand somehow remained free from annealing and could itself be used as a template for a second round of reproduction, the resulting complement of the complementary RNA would actually be a duplicate of the original RNA template. But again, the copy would be annealed with the complementary RNA, which would interfere with further reproduction. Speaking very hypothetically, if this process could repeat without inhibition, exponential reproduction of the template RNA could result.

In the fifty years since the work of Spiegelman, little progress has been reported in finding a self-replicating RNA molecule, or even a ribozyme that can produce RNA from an RNA template (with no required protein enzymes). In the lab, this work commonly starts with a fabricated ribozyme (not produced by natural means), another molecule of RNA as the template, and activated ribonucleotide building blocks. Early efforts could only produce complement RNA from select templates [141]. The complement RNA that formed after the first round (if it could be separated from the template) was itself unacceptable as a template for a second round of copying. Thus, it was not possible to reproduce the original template RNA. Recently, researchers have made claims about vastly improved ribozymes obtained from guided evolutionary processes (i.e., starting with a known ribozyme, creating a variety of slightly different RNAs, and selecting via the intelligence of the investigator those RNAs that have the preferred capabilities) [142, 143]. These ribozymes can produce complementary RNA from a variety of RNA templates, even folded structures, but they still cannot reproduce the ribozyme itself and still struggle with the pesky problem of RNA annealing. Further, this approach does not explain how the ribozyme or template first came into existence. The most successful ribozyme for RNA reproduction to date, reported by Attwater and colleagues in 2018, is actually a combination of two RNA molecules—one composed of 135 ribonucleotides and the other composed of 153 ribonucleotides [143]. The most successful ribozyme is therefore quite complex, requiring the duplication of two RNAs, not just one.

The appearance of the first copy of these complex molecules must also be explained by natural abiotic processes. Such processes strictly cannot include any form of chemical evolution because that is the very process we are trying to initiate. Let's assume that Attwater's ribozyme (the most successful ribozyme to date) was able to copy itself exponentially, so all that is needed is a natural explanation for the arrival of the two RNA molecules in the ribozyme. Let's make it even simpler by requiring only the arrival of the smaller RNA molecule, containing 135 ribonucleotides. Let's also assume that we have an endless supply of activated, concentrated ribonucleotides; that the ribonucleotides are homochiral and they spontaneously link together via the desired bonds to produce RNA; and after the growing chain reaches 135 ribonucleotides, the molecule stops growing. What would it take under these very generous assumptions to find the 135 ribonucleotide RNA needed for Attwater's ribozyme? The chance of arriving at the correct RNA is one in 4^{135}, or one chance in 1.9×10^{81}. As mentioned in Chapter 7, this is similar to the total number of atoms in the known universe. Creation of one copy of each of 1.9×10^{81} possible RNA molecules, each containing 135 ribonucleotides, would therefore require more material than the mass of the universe. Hopefully, this places a rational perspective on the chances of obtaining a self-replicating RNA.

You might be wondering: If two copies of a ribozyme are required to initiate a duplication process (one to act as the template and the other to act as the ribozyme), why wouldn't the process that provided two copies simply produce lots of copies, so we don't need this type of reproduction process after all? That is a good question. The answer, of course, is that you can't get the original two copies through natural abiotic processes in the first place—especially if each copy is a complex molecule such as a combination of 135 ribonucleotides and 153 ribonucleotides.

Perhaps a second approach to RNA replication would be a single RNA ribozyme that could make a copy of itself from a pool of monomers. If complementary monomers naturally line up beside the ribozyme, and the ribozyme itself has the ability to polymerize the monomers, an RNA molecule that is complementary to the ribozyme could be produced. However, for a biopolymer to have some enzymatic or catalytic properties, it needs to be stable in a folded 3-D structure, the 3-D structure being highly specific to encourage a chemical reaction. But in order to reproduce itself, the biopolymer needs to be unfolded, lying in a simple linear chain, so the complementary monomers can align properly and be polymerized. Thus, it is very difficult for the molecule to be ready to reproduce (i.e., act as a ribozyme) and to be ready to be reproduced (i.e., maintain a linear chain) at the same time.

You might wonder whether it is possible for one end of an RNA to serve as an enzyme while the other end of the RNA is a linear chain. Perhaps a helpful analogy for this concept is the goal of washing your arms with a bar of soap. You could hold the bar of soap in your right hand (i.e., this is the enzymatic portion of the RNA molecule) and wash your left hand and arm, but you cannot wash your left hand if it is clenched into a fist—you first have to open your left hand (i.e., the unfolded linear chain at the opposite end of the RNA). So far, so good. The trouble arises as you try to wash your right arm with the bar of soap in your right hand. Similarly, the enzymatic end of the RNA molecule could possibly polymerize the monomers at the opposite end of the RNA, but this process would have to stop somewhere along the RNA because it would not be possible for the enzymatic end of the molecule to operate on itself.

Perhaps both ends of the molecule could function separately as enzymes, where one end facilitates duplication of the other end. This is analogous to switching the bar of soap to the left hand in order to wash the right arm. However, this would require a means of preferentially unfolding a first half of the molecule during its reproduction, then allowing that first half to fold back into its enzymatic 3-D shape (which would also require removal of the new complement or antisense RNA fragment in order to allow folding), while the other half is unfolded for reproduction. Rather unlikely. Maybe a "helper" molecule could facilitate the unfolding. But then we are back to requiring two molecules to appear simultaneously, and this helper molecule would have to operate on only one-half of the RNA at a time.

It would seem that even a vivid imagination has a difficult time arriving at a viable pathway for a self-replicating RNA—that is, unless the vivid imagination includes the ability to dismiss inconvenient truths. As we have mentioned, Addy Pross dismissed inconvenient truths in his interpretation of Spiegelman's work to conclude that "molecular self-replication reaction is a reality."

Another False Hope

A highly touted report of an RNA ribozyme that could reproduce itself appeared in 2009 [144]. The title "Self-Sustained Replication of an RNA Enzyme" seemed to proclaim proof for abiotic reproduction of RNA. However, three serious limitations cast a shadow on this work. First, the authors did not suggest how the process could have started in a prebiotic world—how the first version of the ribozyme (composed of about 76 ribonucleotides) could have been produced. Second, the molecules that the ribozyme operated upon (i.e., the substrates) included preprepared, fully formed ribozymes split into two halves and the exact complement of the fully formed ribozyme split into two halves. In other words, the solution contained one complete ribozyme and many copies of each of four half-ribozymes. The complete ribozyme first created a single bond joining halves 1 and 2, producing a complementary copy of itself. The complementary ribozyme then acted to create a single bond joining halves 3 and 4, producing a copy of the original ribozyme. Some other process had to produce the four half-ribozymes with high purity. A third limitation comes from the observation that this process of replication cannot experience chemical evolution: it only combines two preexisting substrates. For chemical evolution to occur, errors in replication (i.e., mutations) must lead to a selective advantage, such as faster reproduction (a type of natural selection), and be passed to their progeny so that improvements will dominate the population over time ("survival of the fittest"). In the process of RNA replication described in this paper, variations in the components could have resulted in an improved ribozyme, but the improved ribozyme could not pass its improvement on to the next generation (the next two half-ribozymes that it joins). The improved ribozyme, like its predecessors, simply combines two components, not necessarily creating copies of its new and improved self. This is because the supply of components cannot "evolve" themselves because they cannot receive feedback (through natural selection) about which versions of the components are preferred.

Beating a Dead Horse

The concept of a self-replicating RNA faces several other challenges. The rate of synthesis must exceed the rate of degradation, and RNA is easily degraded. The accuracy of the reproduction has to occur within a limited range: too much accuracy reduces the availability of random mutations to create advantages; too little accuracy leads to a mess and the loss of any accumulated function. Also, each inaccurate monomer that is added to a growing chain can slow the process of reproduction. The monomers must be concentrated and pure (challenges beyond homochirality). The monomers must be in an activated form, ready to undergo reactions, but activation implies instability, which can cause undesirable side-reactions. Finally, high concentrations of magnesium are necessary, but this is geochemically unrealistic and magnesium causes breakdown of RNA via hydrolysis [145].

To summarize, decades of research have failed to provide a scenario for abiotic arrival of self-replicating molecules. Even within living organisms, no molecule can reproduce itself—this requires a suite of other molecules, typically involving proteins. This should be very discouraging for abiogenesis because abiogenesis not only requires self-replicating molecules—it also requires the process of self-replication to be pervasive and prosperous. The process has to be responsible for the gradual evolution of very complex molecules, involving thousands of generations of accumulated slight modifications, with every one of the thousands of generations being capable of reproducing themselves, and with advantages accumulating over generations such that natural selection eventually produced complex molecules with sufficient genotype and phenotype to begin the process of life. For this to be true, self-replicating molecules should be the norm—ubiquitous and unavoidable. One should hardly be able to work with RNA without encountering yet another self-replicating RNA. Yet not one has been found in over fifty years of trying. Despite this, supporters of abiogenesis like Addy Pross are able to conclude that "life on Earth emerged through the enormous kinetic power of the replication reaction acting on unidentified, but simple replicating systems, apparently composed of chain-like oligomeric substances, RNA or RNA-like, capable of mutation and complexification" ([66], 183). The supporters of abiogenesis have powerful imaginations, but their imagination and observable reality simply could not be more discordant.

Chapter 12

Nucleotide Sequences Forming Useful Code

In DNA and RNA, no chemical or physical forces impose a preferred sequence or pattern upon the chain of nucleotides. In other words, each base can be followed or preceded by any other base without bias, just as the bits and bytes of information on a computer are free to represent any sequence without bias. This characteristic of DNA and RNA is critical—in fact, essential—for DNA and RNA to serve as unconstrained information carriers. However, this property also obscures any natural explanation for the information content of life—the molecules themselves provide no explanation for the highly specific sequence of nucleotides required to code for specific biologic functions. Only two materialistic explanations[32] have been proposed for the information content of life: fortuitous random arrangements that happen to be functional or the combination of replication, random mutations, and natural selection to improve existing functionality over time.

---

32. A materialistic explanation results from viewing matter and energy as the only fundamental realities.

Wishing upon a Galaxy

As we discussed in Chapter 11, before the hypothetical first self-replicating molecule existed, fortuitous random arrangement was the only possible materialistic explanation. We concluded that obtaining an RNA molecule with a specific sequence of 135 nucleotides through a purely random process would require more material than the mass of the entire universe, and this conclusion was obtained under the highly beneficial but absurd assumptions that the mass of the entire universe consisted of RNA molecules that were homochiral and homolinked and that each consisted of 135 nucleotides.

What if many similar RNA molecules could have similar function—not just one very specific molecule? Many slight variations of the desired molecule could result in similar function. This could be a potential counterargument for the extreme improbability of a specific functional RNA molecule emerging randomly from a prebiotic soup. However, even if there were billions of RNA molecules with similar function, the odds that a random molecule could perform that function remain infinitesimal. To put it in perspective, rather than requiring the mass of the entire universe to be composed of RNA to have one useful molecule, we might now require only the mass of one galaxy to be composed of RNA to have one useful molecule. Such odds certainly do not inspire confidence in the materialistic story.

Douglas Axe, while serving as a research scientist at Cambridge, addressed a similar issue for proteins. He studied β-lactamase, a protein that bacteria produce to defend themselves against penicillin. Axe found that the likelihood of randomly arranging 153 amino acids into a protein domain that performed a similar function as β-lactamase was on the order of one in 10^{77} [146], similar to the chance of finding one specific atom in the universe. In a similar analysis of protein function, MIT researchers

John Reidhaar-Olson and Robert Sauer estimated the proportion of proteins composed of ninety-two amino acids that form a functional lambda repressor fold[33] to be one in 10^{63} [147]. The rational conclusion is that randomly arranged biopolymers offer no hope for the arrival of useful information or functional molecules.

Chemical Evolution to the Rescue?

If we begin this chapter by assuming that all prior challenges on the Stairway to Life have been addressed, rather than properly multiplying the improbability of all prior challenges, we must assume that the first "gene" has already been produced. The first "gene" would be a self-replicating molecule of RNA containing both the code and the catalytic ability to reproduce itself from a pool of monomers. Once a self-replicating RNA is available, the second proposed materialistic explanation for the information content of life—the combination of random mutations and natural selection—is expected to dominate and explain the complexification of all of life. Here, a vast series of consecutive small modifications must take place, with the modifications leading to improvements in function over time because the improved molecules must outcompete all predecessors.

To advance in the direction of any known life-form, additional genes must have developed over time through the process of chemical evolution. A self-replicating RNA molecule must have evolved the additional capability to catalyze a reaction, such as assisting in the production of nucleotide building blocks. One can imagine two possibilities here: one self-replicating RNA that evolved multiple functions (multiple "genes" in one RNA) or several RNA molecules that each evolved unique functions (multiple "genes"

---

33. A lambda repressor is a protein coded by a bacterial virus that regulates the transcription of DNA. The lambda repressor fold is a 3-D structure of the lambda repressor protein that binds to DNA.

spread among several RNAs, each capable of self-replication or of being replicated by another RNA). For the first possibility, the experimental evidence of Spiegelman's Monster from Chapter 11 stands in stark contrast. In this empirical example, chemical evolution over time (albeit with the help of a complex protein enzyme) resulted in dramatic simplification and size reduction of the RNA molecule, not the required complexification and size increase. This occurred because molecules that can be reproduced rapidly will naturally dominate over molecules that are reproduced slowly. Common sense and thermodynamics agree that small molecules would be reproduced more rapidly [148]. Indeed, Spiegelman's Monster "devolved" into the smallest molecule that was able to be reproduced by the enzyme, losing information and function along the way. Thus, simplification, rather than complexification, dominates chemical evolution. The concept of a self-reproducing molecule that gains function, reproductive "fitness," and complexity over a large number of generations not only lacks experimental support—it contradicts common sense and strains the imagination.

The second possibility, that of several self-replicating RNA molecules with unique functions (multiple "genes" spread among several RNAs), also strains the imagination. The concept of chemical evolution involves a self-replicating molecule gaining function over time, outcompeting all rivals so that it dominates the population. How, then, in the midst of a survival-of-the-fittest competition, can we arrive at multiple RNAs with unique functions that coexist in harmony? We require a highly competitive environment to evolve useful molecules, but that same competitive environment must constrain the variety of useful molecules. In biological evolution, natural selection is thought to provide a diversity of organisms that fill distinct ecological niches. In prebiotic chemical evolution, all molecules compete for the same resources: the building blocks of RNA and the ribozyme that reproduces RNA.

This direct competition produces a "winner-takes-all" scenario that inhibits diversification.

The "Top-Down" Approach

Thus far, we have attempted a "bottom-up" approach to the prebiotic assembly of first life, beginning this chapter with the assumption of a first self-replicating molecule or a first "gene" and discussing the possibilities of forming multiple genes. At this point, a change in perspective to a "top-down" approach may help to assess the scope of necessary gene formation to start life. We mentioned that the simplest known life-form that autonomously reproduces is *Mycoplasma genitalium*, with 580,070 base pairs of DNA and 468 genes [52]. After Craig Venter completed *Synthia*, whose genomic DNA was derived from *Myco* and encodes about one thousand genes, he set out to find the simplest autonomously reproducing form of synthetic life. The goal was to arrive at the minimum number of genes and the minimum complexity that could sustain independent life. In 2016, Venter's team published their findings on the simplest living form of *Synthia*, which contains 513,000 base pairs of DNA and 473 genes, but requires more than twice the time to reproduce [51].

As genes are stripped away, the cell becomes less robust. The cell may be able to survive in controlled laboratory environments but not out in the wild when faced with an environmental stress or when it must synthesize many building blocks or nutrients itself. Even intact mycoplasmas are typically found in animal hosts where nutrients are readily available and the environment is somewhat controlled (perhaps you can guess where *Mycoplasma genitalium* likes to hang out). Venter's team admitted that their minimal form of *Synthia* required coddling: "Under less permissive conditions, we expect that additional genes will be required" [51]. We can predict that future efforts to identify a minimal gene set may succeed in demonstrating autonomous reproduction in life-forms with fewer required genes. However, evaluation of these life-forms under a variety of environmental stressors will reveal severe constraints to the minimal organism's survival.

Therefore, a "top-down" approach to life, based on all empiric observations to date, requires at least hundreds of genes—likely in the range of four hundred essential genes—for independent life. The fewer the genes, the greater the requirements for a controlled and privileged environment.

Returning to the "bottom-up" approach, remember that the first "gene" is thought to be a self-replicating RNA, an entity that exists only in the imagination, although we began this chapter under the assumption that it existed. The rich imagination of those who support abiogenesis then envisions either fortuitous random arrangements or random mutations and natural selection to produce hundreds of diverse genes living in harmony in a highly favorable and pampered "incubator" environment that persisted over millions of years, giving birth to the first independent and autonomously reproducing cell. Extraordinary imagination is required to arrive at such a scenario, and extraordinary faith (in lieu of scientific evidence) coupled with the repression of rational thought is required to adopt this explanation for life.

However, even if we are given hundreds of genes, we are still far from the start of life. We have thus far considered only half of the steps on the Stairway to Life. As we will see, life requires much more than the mere availability of genes.

Chapter 13
Means of Gene Regulation

U nder the assumption that all prior steps on the Stairway to Life have been achieved, we now have biopolymers such as RNA that contain useful information (i.e., genes) and are easily reproduced. We begin this chapter under the assumption that we have hundreds of "genes," either one gene in each RNA molecule or combinations of genes in fewer RNA molecules. At this point, each RNA molecule must serve both as genotype and phenotype (i.e., both storing information and performing a function). For convenience, we will refer to these molecules as ribozymes.

The hypothetical chemical evolution of these ribozymes required a competition such that one type of ribozyme dominated over all rivals. In theory, a ribozyme could dominate over others if it had any number of advantages, such as the ability to function under a broader set of environmental conditions, the ability to destroy rival ribozymes, or if it replicated the fastest or was more stable. While the hypothetical characteristics of hypothetical ribozymes might be difficult to assess, the advantageous characteristic that seems to have been proposed most often by abiogenesis proponents (and the characteristic we will consider as an example) is the ability to replicate the fastest. After all, if one type of ribozyme were to self-replicate faster than others, it should eventually "win" in the competition for resources under evolutionary theory. However, the unconstrained competition that supposedly produced these ribozymes would soon deplete resources and fill the available space with many copies of a single ribozyme. This situation is analogous to cancer: the rapid reproduction of an entity that selfishly hoards all resources and performs no cooperative function, ultimately leading to destruction. To progress toward a living organism, this situation must somehow be transformed from a cancer-like environment into an environment of synergistic molecular activity, balanced production of ribozymes, and homeostasis.[34] Living organisms require highly coordinated, selfless molecular activity—more like an orchestra and less like an oligarchy. This transformation comes from a higher level of organization: the regulation of genes.

How to Regulate a Gene

Like a furnace without a thermostat, an unregulated gene can waste energy and resources and create an environment that is detrimental to life. Like a thermostat, the regulation of a gene often requires at least three components: 1) a means of sensing (e.g., temperature sensed via a thermometer), 2) a means of making a decision based on the sensed value (e.g., temperature is sufficiently high or is too low), and 3) a means of acting on the decision to affect the desired control. This coordination of separate components toward a shared purpose poses a challenge for abiotic explanations.

To provide an example, the reader may forgive us for preferring to refer to known functions of existing life-forms, rather than remaining in the hypothetical realm of unobservable prebiotic

---

34. Homeostasis involves the maintenance of internal stability despite environmental fluctuations and disruptions.

chemistry. *E. coli* can manufacture the amino acid tryptophan by producing the enzyme tryptophan synthase. Production of this enzyme requires precious resources that the cell would prefer to conserve. As a result, the cell carefully regulates production—a far better approach than continuous full-speed production of the enzyme. In the cell, freely available tryptophan produces negative feedback for production of tryptophan synthase, thus conserving resources. To accomplish this, *E. coli* have another gene that codes for a regulatory protein called "TrpR," or "tryptophan repressor" [149]. When the TrpR protein senses the presence of available tryptophan, the protein becomes activated (i.e., changes shape) and binds to the DNA immediately preceding the genes for tryptophan synthase. The attachment of activated TrpR to this regulatory segment of DNA inhibits tryptophan synthase production, thus stopping the production of tryptophan. The simple summary is that freely available tryptophan inhibits the production of tryptophan via specific information stored in DNA. As a result of this ingenious regulatory system with its multiple coordinated components, the level of tryptophan is maintained at the correct level for cellular function.

Returning to the hypothetical prebiotic world, perhaps one or several ribozymes could similarly be involved in the production of an essential nutrient. But when this nutrient is readily available, uninhibited production of the ribozymes and the nutrient would quickly use up available resources. Conservation of resources can be achieved by repressing the ribozymes that produce the nutrient. This would require some method of sensing the nutrient and inhibiting the associated ribozymes. The sensing of the nutrient must be highly specific, or else a similar "imposter" molecule could wrongly inhibit production of the essential nutrient and bring metabolic activity to an inappropriate halt. Highly specific molecular interactions such as this imply the presence of relatively complex molecules. For example, the TrpR protein that senses tryptophan in *E. coli* is composed of 107 amino acids that are encoded by 321 nucleotides of DNA/RNA [149]. Applying this to prebiotic ribozymes, we should expect many additional nucleotides of RNA added to each ribozyme to perform a regulatory function.

The *glmS* gene of the bacteria *Bacillus subtilis* provides another real-life example of regulation—in this case with added RNA serving a regulatory purpose. Here, a segment of RNA (approximately seventy-five nucleotides) is added to a messenger RNA that codes for a metabolic enzyme. When the additional RNA segment senses a metabolic product of the enzyme, it changes shape and cuts the messenger RNA to inactivate it, thus preventing additional production of the enzyme [150]. In a prebiotic self-replicator world, this additional length of RNA for regulation must be very specific in sensing a cofactor, must be explained either by random appearance or the accumulation of random errors and natural selection, and must neither significantly slow the speed of ribozyme reproduction nor interfere with the normal catalytic function of the ribozyme. The investigators who first described this RNA-based regulatory mechanism interpreted their finding as supportive of abiogenesis: "The central functions of ribozymes in modern organisms support the hypothesis that life passed through an 'RNA world' before the emergence of proteins and DNA" [150]. However, they offer no mechanism for how such a regulatory RNA could have arrived, other than a passing acknowledgement of "natural evolutionary processes."

Homeland Security

Restriction systems (mentioned in Chapter 4) are another regulatory mechanism that pose an even greater challenge for abiotic arrival. Even very simplistic life-forms like *Myco* produce enzymes

called restriction endonucleases that break DNA at specific sites—
specific patterns of DNA that are a perfect match to the enzyme's
recognition site. Restriction enzymes are used to protect the cell
from foreign DNA, such as the *Synthia* DNA that was produced by
yeast and injected into *Capri* in Venter's experiment.

Imagine that a home security system included a sophisticated
but rather extreme defense mechanism: a robot that roams the
house, identifying any humans and killing them. The system is
sophisticated because it is highly accurate at targeting only humans—it will never kill pets, plants, or anything else that is not
human. This is clearly a potent defense system; the only remaining
issue is that it will certainly kill the owners of the house. Similarly,
endonucleases will destroy any DNA that matches a specific targeted pattern. Unfortunately, the cell's own DNA commonly has
regions that match the targeted sequence of the endonuclease.
Unregulated production of these enzymes would therefore be
suicidal.

Returning to our home security system, suppose we improve
the system by acquiring a second robot that also searches the
house for humans and is very accurate at identifying them. When
the second robot finds a human, it attaches an identifying tag to
the human. This tag protects the human because the first robot
will only kill humans who do not have the tag. Together, the two
robots provide a very effective defense system, as long as the second robot is deployed first, for a short period of time, and the second robot is deployed again in the event that the family expands
or has guests for dinner. In cells, the analogous identifying tag is
the methylation of DNA via specific methyltransferase enzymes.
The methyltransferase and endonuclease enzymes are perfectly
complementary in that they target the same specific sequence
of DNA, one tagging it for protection and the other destroying
the DNA if there is no tag. As you can imagine, a more effective

defense against foreign DNA would target more patterns of DNA, but this would also increase the risk of destroying the cell's own DNA. This is the case in extant life [151]. It should now be clear that the methyltransferase must be produced by the cell before the endonuclease can be produced. These enzymes must be carefully regulated to avoid the death of the cell while destroying intruders.

We must now ask the question: How could such a complex methyltransferase/endonuclease system first appear from purely materialistic processes (spontaneous generation or evolution)? Production of only the methyltransferase offers no benefit to the cell and would add a burden. Production of only the endonuclease would lead to cell death. Only the simultaneous acquisition of the DNA for each methyltransferase/endonuclease complementary pair, together with mechanisms for careful regulation of their production, could confer a benefit to the cell. Many similar examples of toxin-antitoxin pairs exist in life. These toxin-antitoxin systems play important cellular functions, including maintaining plasmids, responding to stress, arresting and persisting bacterial growth, shaping prokaryotic genomes [151], protecting against phage infection [152–155], and maintaining the integrity of the genomes. The existence of toxin-antitoxin gene pairs poses a serious challenge for purely materialistic origins.

Waiter, There's a Parasite in My Soup

You may be wondering why a prebiotic system should have any interest in toxin-antitoxin systems. Returning to our hypothetical set of prebiotic ribozymes, imagine a small invading parasitic RNA that serves no function but either reproduces itself very rapidly or is reproduced very rapidly by the existing ribozymes. This RNA acts like a cancer, reproducing exponentially, outcompeting all other RNAs, and depleting resources but producing nothing of value. A prebiotic system that is progressing toward life would be destroyed by such a parasitic RNA. Here's the catch: because the parasitic RNA is small, whereas useful RNAs will be longer, for every useful RNA molecule that arises by random arrangement, there will be billions upon billions of smaller parasitic RNAs that arise by random arrangement. The vast predominance of parasitic RNAs would hinder the formation of any useful ribozymes. An effective protection would be a ribozyme that acts like an endonuclease, breaking up the parasitic RNA before it can reproduce and wreak havoc. But the availability of this RNA endonuclease also runs the risk of destroying useful molecules that have the same matching sequence of RNA. This necessitates the availability of another RNA that acts to protect the useful molecules. As in the example above, the RNA endonuclease and protecting RNA would require nearly simultaneous arrival and careful regulation to provide a net benefit, yet without them, prebiotic progress toward life could be severely hindered by a simple parasitic RNA.

The required transformation of the prebiotic world from survival of the fittest type of molecule to the regulation, symbiosis, and homeostasis of hundreds of distinct molecules requires an additional layer of information content. In a sense, each step in the Stairway to Life requires an additional layer of information and organization to progress from chemistry to biology. Although we can readily observe this additional layer of regulatory information at work in all known life, we have no materialistic explanation for the arrival of this information. Materialistic explanations are especially strained in cases like restriction systems, which require the simultaneous arrival of multiple regulated components to produce a benefit rather than a detriment.

Chapter 14

Means for Repairing Biopolymers

Assuming that the challenges of all prior chapters have been overcome, we have now amassed a significant quantity of prebiotic information stored in molecules. The current abiogenesis story ascribes millions of years, perhaps hundreds of millions of years, for the accumulation of this information. The immensity of deep time plays the role of the protagonist in the drama of abiogenesis. The story goes something like this: the accumulation of information required for each step is highly improbable, but given enough time, anything could happen. Unbeknownst to the playwright, their hero has a dark side: time is a subversive agent intent on destroying—not accumulating—information. Information generally degrades over time. For example, what fraction of literary works have survived from ancient Persia? Similarly, how many people remember what they had for lunch last Monday? Maintenance of information over time requires targeted application of energy. Given a focused application of human energy, more literary works from ancient Persia could have survived. For abiogenesis, maintenance of information over deep time in a prebiotic world would require very specific application of energy to preserve the information despite natural degradative processes.

Within our short lifetime, the information stored in our DNA faces a continuous barrage of attacks from radiation, oxidation, alkylation, chemical mutagens, pathogens, and water. Every day, the DNA in a typical human cell faces an estimated 2,000–10,000 depurinations [110, 111], 600 depyrimidinations [156], 10,000 cases of oxidative damage [157], 55,000 single-strand breaks [158], and 10 double-strand breaks [159].

Molecular Maintenance Plan

Fortunately, living organisms are endowed with a wide variety of specialized DNA repair mechanisms to counteract these daily attacks: base excision repair, nucleotide excision repair, homologous recombination repair, mismatch repair, photoreactivation, nonhomologous end joining, translesion synthesis [160], and processing by the MRN complex [161].[35] The base excision repair mechanism (Figure 12) occurs in prokaryotes and eukaryotes and requires the coordinated efforts of at least five enzymes to make small repairs to DNA [110, 162]. The nucleotide excision repair mechanism, also highly prevalent throughout life, targets more extensive damage. In *E. coli*, nucleotide excision repair requires five enzymes to replace a strip of twelve nucleotides when DNA damage is discovered [163]. These repair pathways preserve information via very specific applications of energy; production and function of the enzymes both require energy.

---

35. The MRN complex is indeed complex. It is also known as the complex of meiotic recombination 11 homolog 1 (MRE11), ATP-binding cassette–ATPase (RAD50), and phosphopeptide-binding Nijmegen breakage syndrome protein 1 (NBS1). The MRE11 and RAD50 components are conserved across all domains of life [161].

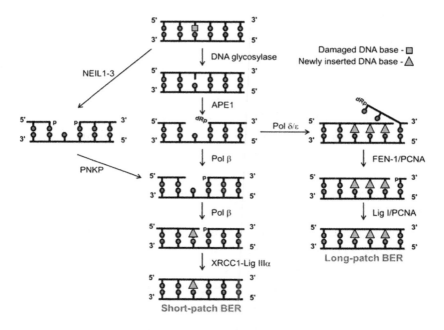

Figure 12. The base excision repair pathway [164]. The short patch pathway repairs a single nucleotide, and the long pathway repairs between two and ten nucleotides. Each step in the paths requires one or more complex protein enzymes (listed adjacent to arrows).

In humans, mutations that result in dysfunction of these DNA repair mechanisms often result in embryonic death. Those who survive face a variety of diseases like progeria, ataxia telangiectasia, Nijmegen breakage syndrome, Werner syndrome, Bloom syndrome, Fanconi anemia, xeroderma pigmentosum, Cockayne syndrome, and trichothiodystrophy, leading to premature aging, increased risk of cancer, neurologic defects, and growth retardation [165–167].

In addition to repairing damage to existing DNA, living organisms have mechanisms to correct errors during reproduction.

Bacteria have three types of DNA polymerase, all capable of detecting an incorrect base pairing, backing up one step to excise the incorrect nucleotide, and then progressing forward in a process called proofreading. The proofreading step decreases the error rate in bacteria from approximately one error in 100,000 base pairs to one error in 10,000,000 base pairs [160].

The critical importance of DNA repair mechanisms in all living organisms immediately produces a conundrum: the DNA repair mechanisms are themselves encoded in DNA that requires repair mechanisms. Imagine that the world is full of thieves, and you have the world's first idea for a security system that will deter all thieves. You plan to manufacture the security system in a factory. However, as you begin construction on the factory, thieves continuously steal the blueprints, the raw materials, even the funds needed to build the factory. The factory will never be completed, and a security system will never be produced. Similarly, DNA repair mechanisms could not have evolved without the protection of DNA repair mechanisms. And ordinary DNA could not have evolved before DNA repair genes evolved.

RNA: Repair Needed Again

Returning to the hypothetical prebiotic RNA world, our accumulated information remains in the delicate hands of RNA, molecules that are substantially less durable than DNA. The single-stranded RNA structure is inherently less mechanically and thermodynamically stable than double-stranded DNA. The reactive bases in double-stranded DNA are also bonded to each other, keeping them from reacting with other molecules. The extra-hydroxyl group in the pentose ring of RNA makes it more susceptible to hydrolysis, especially in an alkaline environment. A weak solution of sodium hydroxide will destroy RNA but will not damage DNA. Finally, replacement of thymine in DNA with uracil in

RNA makes RNA more sensitive to radioactive mutation. If DNA in living organisms requires active repair mechanisms, the more delicate prebiotic RNA, it stands to reason, must also require active repair mechanisms.

Eigen's Paradox

In Chapter 11, we mentioned how the hypothetical process of RNA self-replication must introduce some errors to provide the raw materials for chemical evolution. Indeed, all replication processes introduce some errors. In 1971, Nobel Laureate Manfred Eigen described how the length of a prebiotic information molecule like RNA must fundamentally be limited according to the error rate during replication [168]. Reproduction of longer molecules introduces more errors, and too many errors would lead to an exponential increase in errors over many generations—an error catastrophe. Eigen observed that living organisms require error correction during replication to avoid error catastrophe in long DNA molecules. Yet the error-correction mechanisms themselves must be coded in the same lengthy DNA molecules. This led to Eigen's paradox: a self-replicating molecule faces a practical size limit of about one hundred nucleotides unless there are error-correction systems, but the error-correction systems themselves must be coded in molecules that are substantially longer than the practical limit.

Eigen's paradox only addresses errors during replication and the need for error-correction mechanisms during replication. The additional burden of accumulated molecular damage from radiation, oxidation, alkylation, chemical mutagens, pathogens, and water, especially over deep time, and the associated requirement for additional molecular-repair mechanisms, greatly compounds Eigen's paradox.

What we need for abiogenesis is a self-replicating RNA that has just the right error rate during reproduction, resulting in information gain over millions of years with a replication rate that somehow improves over time and the preservation of information via repair mechanisms that spontaneously appear.

What we have is the absence of a self-replicating molecule, evidence that replication processes prefer shortening and simplification of RNA over time, known instability of RNA over time, and no hope of arriving at the required repair mechanisms. All empiric observations tell us that organic molecules, once life has ended, rapidly devolve into a useless mixture, referred to as "asphalt." How, then, can we rationally expect organic molecules to progress naturally toward complexity and organization in the absence of life?

Chapter 15

Selectively Permeable Membranes

Supporters of abiogenesis attempt to simplify the requirements for life, arguing that minimal prototype structures could suffice for each component of early life. Cell membranes seem to be an easy target. In all living organisms, the cell membrane consists of a phospholipid bilayer.[36] In Chapter 7, we described how phospholipids naturally collect into a structure of two adjacent sheets (a bilayer) in water, with the water-hating (i.e., hydrophobic) lipid components of the two sheets facing each other (in the center of the bilayer, where there is no water) and the phosphate components forming the outer surfaces, where there is water. The edges of this bilayer are in a high-energy state because their hydrophobic regions are exposed to water. The bilayer can therefore spontaneously transform into a lower-energy state, sometimes forming a spherical shell of bilayer, otherwise known as a vesicle.[37]

Because phospholipids can spontaneously form vesicles in water, it would seem that membranes are one component of life that is easy to explain by purely natural processes. However, no

---

36. With the possible exception of a few species of archaea [169].
37. In reality, the spontaneous formation of a single bilayer is exceedingly rare; multilamellar structures or stacks of bilayers predominate [170].

living organism could survive with such a simple cell membrane. Although this simple membrane effectively creates spatial separation (keeping some molecules in and other molecules out) and allows small molecules like oxygen, water, and carbon dioxide to pass through, charged molecules and larger molecules like carbohydrates, amino acids, phosphate, nucleobases, and waste products struggle to cross the membrane barrier [171]. A living cell requires a continuous supply of building materials and energy and requires the removal of waste. Such a tight cell membrane would therefore serve only as a tomb to sequester decaying components. We also note that vesicles composed of a single phospholipid bilayer are metastable at best, being quite sensitive to temperature [172]. The single bilayer can rapidly transition to a multilamellar structure (i.e., stacks of bilayers), thus destroying the cell. Living organisms can actively modify the phospholipid composition of their membranes in response to temperature changes to maintain stability of their single-bilayer membranes, a process sometimes called homeoviscous adaptation [173–176].

Requirements for Membranes

To start or sustain life, cell membranes must meet a complex set of conflicting requirements. As we will learn in Chapter 16, one of the essential requirements of a membrane is to maintain a higher concentration of protons on one side relative to the other (a proton gradient). If the membranes in your body suddenly lost their proton gradients, you would not be able to finish reading this paragraph and your life would be unrecoverable within minutes. Cyanide poisoning works by this method. Thus, membranes must be tight enough to block the passage of protons. However, membranes must also allow much larger cellular building materials, sources of energy, and communications from the outside world to pass in, and waste products and communications to the outside world to pass out. And the passage of these larger molecules must be controlled: food and building materials only transport into the cell, waste products only transport out of the cell, and everything occurs in moderation to maintain homeostasis. The membranes of living organisms satisfy these conflicting requirements by way of specialized pores in the membrane that are composed of proteins. In fact, proteins account for approximately half of the mass of cell membranes in prokaryotes [177], and even the simplest known autonomously reproducing cell, *Mycoplasma genitalium*, operates with about 140 different proteins integrated into its membrane [52]. Of all the known proteins produced by living organisms, approximately one-third operate within membranes [178].

Requirements for Transmembrane Pores

A nonspecific membrane pore that is always open would destroy the proton gradient. Therefore, pores must be highly specific, and most pores open only when triggered to open. Aquaporins, as the name suggests, are specialized membrane pores that allow water transfer across the membrane [179]. Although water can diffuse slowly across the phospholipid bilayer, a wide variety of life-forms from bacteria to fungi to mammals require more rapid transport of water. However, these organisms must maintain a proton gradient across the membrane. During a thunderstorm, everyone must get out of the swimming pool because water conducts electricity. Similarly, a stream of water molecules passing through a membrane pore acts like a conductive wire for the passage of protons. Yet aquaporins allow water to pass through the membrane while blocking the passage of protons. This occurs via precise manipulation of each water molecule, such that each molecule is rotated perpendicular to the orientation that would be required for conduction of protons [180, 181].

To maintain a proton gradient and other unnatural concentration gradients across the membrane, molecules must be pushed across the membrane against natural forces of diffusion. This requires a source of energy. Think of an automatic revolving door in a building that senses the presence of an approaching pedestrian and activates a motor to pass the pedestrian into or out of a building. To improve upon this analogy, we must have people crowded inside the building who would like to get out, but the revolving door serves only to catch people walking down the street and force them into the building.

Cells contain these specific "automated revolving doors" for a wide variety of molecules. One of the most familiar and highly conserved families of specialized transmembrane pores is ATP-binding cassette (ABC) transporters [182]. ABC transporters are composed of multiple subunits of proteins: at least one that traverses the membrane and is embedded in it and at least one that is inside the cell and serves to extract energy from ATP (see Figure 13). Recently, researchers have achieved a full understanding of the shape changes that occur in one ABC transporter that is used by *E. coli* to export a peptide with the alluring name Mccj25 [183]. At the beginning of the export cycle, the ATP-binding portion is open into the cell. When a molecule of Mccj25 enters the pore, the binding of two ATP molecules triggers closure of the pore inside the cell and opening of the transmembrane subunit to release the Mccj25 to the outside of the cell.[38] The energy of the ATP is then used to close the transmembrane subunit and reopen the inner portion of the pore, preparing the transporter for another cycle.

---

38. Interestingly, Mccj25 is produced by *E. coli* when faced with starvation. Mccj25 is a toxin that blocks RNA polymerase and is produced by *E. coli* with the intention of killing any nearby cells so that more nutrients can become available to the *E. coli*. But Mccj25 would also kill the *E. coli* if it were not quickly ejected from the cell.

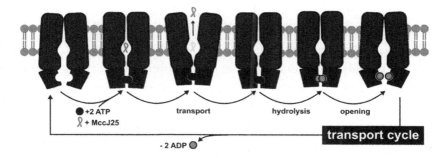

Figure 13. The mechanism of an ABC transporter contained within a cell membrane.

Active and specific transporters like this are essential to transport molecules against concentration gradients while maintaining cell integrity and the proton gradient. As we will see in Chapter 16, the proton gradient is essential to generate ATP, the same ATP that is required to run the ABC transporter. Thus, we have another critical interdependence: the membrane requires embedded proteins to achieve its semipermeable functionality, but the embedded proteins require the semipermeable membrane to produce the ATP that fuels their function.

Insertion of Membrane Pores

You might be wondering: If the membrane is impermeable to large molecules, how can a large protein like an ABC transporter become inserted into the membrane? Size isn't the only challenge here. Proteins that operate in the membrane must start and end with regions (domains) that like to be in water, but the middle sections of membranes repel water and those molecular regions that like to be in water. Thus, to insert the protein, a water-loving region must pass through a water-hating region. Together, the size and repulsion issues create quite a challenge for the insertion of proteins in a membrane, somewhat like trying to drive a well-marked bus for the Real Madrid football team through downtown Barcelona during rush hour.

Across all the diversity of life, most proteins are actively inserted into the membrane by the general secretion pathway, a process that requires DNA, RNA, ribosomes, ATP (or GTP) as a source of energy, and other proteins. The complexity of the general secretion pathway, even in very simple forms of life, should diminish any enthusiasm for abiogenesis. The DNA that codes for the ABC transporter proteins is first transcribed into messenger RNA. A ribosome (which is a complex combination of more than forty proteins and other RNAs) then attaches to the messenger RNA, translating it into a polypeptide. The first portion of the new polypeptide is hydrophobic, like the middle of the cell membrane. This portion is called the signal sequence. A signal recognition particle (composed of proteins and RNA) then attaches to the signal sequence, temporarily halting the ribosome's translation process (or else the completed new protein would fold into a three-dimensional shape, which is more difficult to pass through the membrane). With the help of an additional protein, the emerging polypeptide is introduced to an existing pore in the membrane, which is composed of three proteins (known as the SecYEG translocon). The hydrophobic signal sequence enters the translocon and finds a comfortable position in the middle of the cell membrane, where hydrophobicity is welcome. The ribosome can then complete the translation process, producing a protein that is within the membrane [184, 185]. This description has been greatly simplified to provide a brief overview of the process and a basic appreciation for the complexity, without overwhelming detail. In short, it is not easy to get a protein into the cell membrane.[39]

You may have noticed that the process of inserting a protein into the membrane requires proteins that are already in the membrane (such as the SecYEG translocon). The SecYEG translocon is also inserted into the membrane by another SecYEG translocon. A remaining mystery, then, is how the first SecYEG translocon could have formed and could have been introduced into the first membrane.

The plans for the membrane-bound proteins are encoded in the cell's DNA. Although the DNA specifies the complex sequence of these molecules, it does not specify the localization and the organization of those molecules in the cell membrane. Rather, the overall organization or spatial architecture of the membrane is achieved through inheritance of the progenitor cell's membrane. This includes the inheritance of membrane-bound translocons for inserting new proteins into the membrane.

No cell has ever been observed to generate a complete de novo functional membrane. The membrane surrounding the first *Synthia* was the existing membrane of *Capri*. Membranes are inherited and used as a template for expansion; they are not fabricated from scratch [187, 188]. Franklin Harold, professor emeritus of biochemistry and molecular biology at Colorado State University, observed, "Just as every cell comes from a cell, so does every membrane come from a membrane" ([99], 94). Quite ironically, this quote comes from a book that argues in favor of abiogenesis.

---

39. For completeness, insertases can also insert a handful of proteins into membranes without requiring ATP as an energy source. However, insertases are quite complex (YidC insertase from *E. coli* contains 529 amino acids), generally require the assistance of other proteins, and most commonly work in a coordinated manner with SecYEG translocons [186].

To summarize, the simplest known autonomously reproducing cell, *Mycoplasma genitalium*, has about 140 different proteins integrated into its membrane [52]. Those who support abiogenesis can only attempt to explain the arrival of such complex membranes by departing from observable science, producing elaborative narratives that rely upon imagination and faith ([189] and [64], 137–146). There is no evidence that simplified proto-membranes could meet the requirements for starting life or could complexify over time to successively approximate the complex membranes we observe today. Just as cells only come from cells, membranes only come from membranes.

Chapter 16

Means of Harnessing Energy

I n modern society, electricity pulses through every wall in every house thanks to the burning of coal, natural gas, or petroleum, or the conversion of wind, solar, hydroelectric, or nuclear energy. The wide variety of energy sources are all converted to a familiar format of electricity (e.g., 60Hz and 110–120 volts in the United States). A common use of electricity is to recharge batteries for a wide variety of applications. We have become so dependent on electricity and batteries that life nearly ceases when they are taken away.

Similarly, the activities of a living organism require a continuous source of energy. Life is simply not possible without energy. A fundamental characteristic of life is organization—layers upon layers of organized complexity. Such organization naturally opposes the second law of thermodynamics, which states that net disorder must increase over time in a closed system. Opposing the second law of thermodynamics requires continuous and specific application of energy.

Chemiosmotic Coupling

In living organisms, the general process for harnessing and storing energy, known as "chemiosmotic coupling," is remarkably well conserved.[40] The process shares many similarities with the charging of batteries in our homes. Chemiosmotic coupling starts with various sources of energy (e.g., sunlight; carbon sources like carbohydrates, proteins, or fats; or inorganic sources like sulfur, sulfide, manganese oxide, and ferrous iron) and burns or converts them to produce a consistent format of electricity. In life, the electricity appears as a proton gradient across a membrane; in our homes, the electricity appears as a voltage difference between two wires. The cell uses the proton gradient to charge "batteries" such as adenosine triphosphate (ATP), hence the "coupling" part of chemiosmotic coupling. ATP is a nearly universal battery in life. Once charged, it can be "plugged into" a wide variety of molecular machines to perform a wide variety of functions: activating amino acids for protein synthesis, copying DNA, untangling DNA, breaking bonds, transporting molecules, or contracting muscles. Like rechargeable batteries, ATP cycles frequently between powering gadgets and recharging. Although a human body contains only about sixty grams of ATP at any given moment, it is estimated that humans regenerate approximately their own weight in molecules of ATP every day ([64], 63).

Because chemiosmotic coupling is essential for life and is highly conserved across all of life, abiogenesis must include a purely natural means to arrive at chemiosmotic coupling. This requires a membrane (as just discussed in Chapter 15), a mechanism for

---

40. Fermentation is the one known exception to chemiosmotic coupling. However, fermentation is very limited by itself because it produces waste products that need to be removed by other organisms via chemiosmotic coupling. So fermentation is not considered to be a candidate for energy harnessing by the first cells [64].

pumping protons across the membrane, and a mechanism for producing or "recharging" ATP. The challenge is particularly onerous because these three components are highly complex in all of life and are interdependent to provide energy for life. In other words, the pumping of protons is of no use unless the membrane is there to maintain a gradient of protons. The membrane has no function for energy generation unless there is a mechanism for pumping protons across it. Similarly, the method of ATP production is of no use without a proton gradient across a membrane.

The Electron Transport Chain

Assuming for the moment that a natural means exists for producing the membrane, we next need a means of extracting energy from food to generate a proton gradient. In life, this involves an electron transport chain (except for methanogens and acetogens, as discussed below). The most common electron transport chain includes the coordinated effort of three complexes of molecules that are attached to the membrane. The word "complex" here has a double meaning and cannot be underestimated. The following description (although somewhat technical) is essential to provide some perspective of the complexity of the common electron transport chain.

The three complexes strip electrons (typically from a carbon source of "food") and pass the electrons very carefully down a chain of reactions in a process that simultaneously pumps protons across the membrane. The common waste products are CO_2 and H_2O—similar to the combustion of fuel in your car, except that the cell does not use violent explosions; it uses a careful and extraordinarily precise sequence of about fifteen reactions. Stripping electrons from carbon is not so difficult; harvesting the resulting energy is the real challenge. Electrons are highly reactive and difficult to control. The three complexes handle the electrons like a game of hot potato, quickly passing them from one stop to the next without dropping them. If electrons escape the chain of reactions, free radicals result, causing damage to important biomolecules. If a cell, even a simple bacterium, detects too many free radicals from the electron transport chain, the cell is smart enough to realize that it could become a danger to its neighbors. The altruistic cell responds by entering "programmed cell death mode," otherwise known as apoptosis, wherein an organized and safe disassembly of the cell occurs. The complexity of sensing free radical formation and the resulting apoptosis are another chapter in the complexity of life—one that is beyond the scope of this book.

In the electron transport chain, the extraction of energy by passing the electrons from one step to the next requires proteins of exquisite accuracy. The process involves electron tunneling, a quantum phenomenon that occurs over distances of only a dozen or so angstroms (an angstrom is approximately the diameter of a single hydrogen atom). An increase of one angstrom in distance between steps of the electron transport chain decreases the speed of the reaction by about tenfold ([64], 231). Regressing to our childhood for a moment, the process has some similarity to a Slinky "walking" down a staircase. The Slinky at the top of the stairs has potential energy that dissipates as it descends the steps. But unlike what the Slinky commercials show, we all know how rarely a Slinky succeeds in reaching the bottom of the stairs. Success requires precision and no obstacles; failure means that the Slinky will be stuck on a step and will block the next Slinky from traveling down the steps. The electron transport chain is similar, except with substantially higher precision (each step must be within a few angstroms of the expected distance or else the reaction will stop) and a substantially higher penalty for failure (free radical formation could destroy the step or the entire cell). This implies that very precisely formed and folded proteins must be responsible for the process, calling into question the possibility of arriving at such complex proteins via thousands of successive small innovations, fueled by random mutations and honed by natural selection.

The three complexes are creatively named Complex I (also known as *NADH-Q Oxidoreductase*), Complex III (also known as coenzyme *Q-cytochrome c oxidoreductase*), and Complex IV (also known as *cytochrome c oxidase*) ([190], Chapter 18). Complex II exists but is an alternative entry point to the electron transport chain.

A simplified version of Complex I (Figure 14), as found in the bacterium *Thermus thermophilus*, consists of an assembly of sixteen separate proteins, where each protein is composed of hundreds of amino acids [191]. In contrast, Complex I in eukaryotes requires forty-four separate proteins.[41] For every two electrons shuttled through Complex I, four protons are pumped across the membrane.

The composition of Complex III varies from three proteins in simple organisms [192] to eleven distinct proteins in vertebrates [193]. The passage of two electrons through Complex III also pumps four protons across the membrane.

Complex IV consists of six proteins in simple organisms [194] and fourteen proteins in mammals [195]. Complex IV pumps two protons across the membrane for each pair of electrons that is transferred to oxygen.

---

41. A common misconception of molecular biology is that proteins function as single molecules. In reality, most proteins function only when combined with groups of other proteins, like Lego pieces combined to form a Lego truck. But unlike Legos, the proteins assemble automatically (sometimes requiring the help of other proteins), based on the matching of regions of the proteins that attract each other—positive regions attract negative regions, oily regions prefer to stay together, and water-loving regions prefer to stay together.

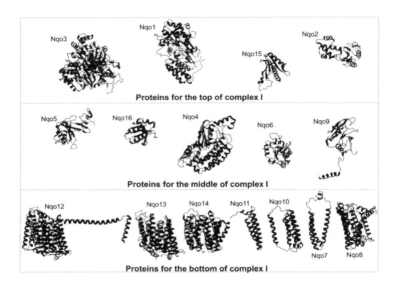

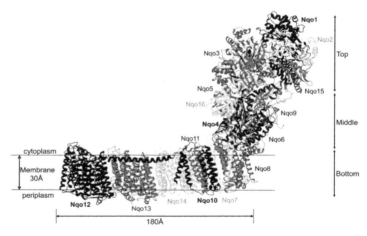

Figure 14. Complex I. *Top:* The sixteen individual proteins in the bacterium *T. thermophilus* that combine to form Complex I. *Bottom:* The combined molecular structure of Complex I. "Cytoplasm" indicates the contents inside the cell membrane, and "periplasm" indicates a space between the cell membrane and the cell wall.

For those who are keeping count, the complete electron transport chain pumps ten protons across the membrane for each transported pair of electrons. Complex I, III, and IV together require a minimum of twenty-five proteins (sixty-nine in mammals) just for the process of pumping protons, and these proteins must fold and combine such that successive "steps" in the electron transport pathway align to within about ten angstroms of each other.

With these three complexes, a proper membrane, and a source of fuel, the cell is now capable of producing electricity. In our houses, electricity typically maintains 110 or 220 volts between two insulated conductors. In mitochondria, the insulating membrane is about fifty angstroms thick, and the voltage difference maintained across the thin membrane is between 0.15 and 0.2 volts. That may not seem like a lot of voltage, but it equates to an electric field of roughly thirty million volts per meter, which is similar in strength to a bolt of lightning.

ATP Synthase

After the formation of a proton gradient across a membrane, charging of the ATP "battery" must next be explained. ATP is produced via ATP synthase (Figure 15), an elegant and fantastically complex molecular machine that is conserved across all of life (although there are minor differences in various forms of life). The simplest known form of ATP synthase (in *E. coli*) consists of at least twenty interconnected protein molecules (eight unique subunits) [196]. John Walker received the Nobel Prize in 1997 for describing the structure of ATP synthase.

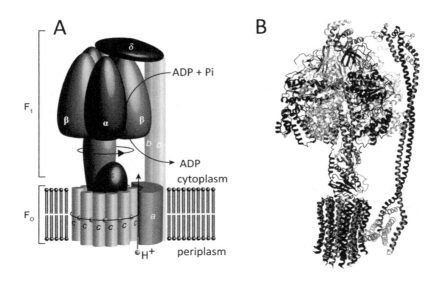

Figure 15. ATP synthase [197]. *A.* A diagram of ATP synthase in *E. coli*, showing the eight labeled subunits and the membrane. *B.* The molecular structure of ATP synthase.

Words and metaphors often fail when attempting to describe a masterpiece. We highly recommend that you take a few moments to review some of the excellent animated tutorials on the mechanism of ATP synthase on YouTube.[42] ATP synthase is an electrical nanomotor with some subunits that remain fixed and other subunits that rotate (see Figure 15). The *a-* and b_2-subunits of ATP synthase are bound within the membrane. The *c*-subunit is actually composed of between ten and fourteen duplicate subunits that surround the driveshaft within the membrane. Protons cross the membrane between the *a-* and *c*-subunits. But this is not a simple

---

42. For example, watch this four-minute video [198]: https://www.youtube.com/watch?v=b_cp8MsnZFA

channel for proton flow. The protons reach the *c*-subunit via an ingress channel, where they attach to each *c*-subunit and cause a conformational change. The conformational change pushes the *c*-subunit away from the stationary *a*-subunit, resulting in angular momentum. A merry-go-round may serve as a useful metaphor. Children (protons) stand in line to enter the merry-go-round. The entrance gate is separated from the exit gate. The merry-go-round has ten seats for ten children. Each child enters the merry-go-round by first holding on to an empty seat, then pushing off the ground as they launch into the seat, providing a boost of angular momentum. Each proton then gets to ride the merry-go-round for one complete rotation, exiting the ride when the *c*-subunit that they are sitting on returns to the *a*-subunit. The egress channel to exit the ride leads to the opposite side of the membrane as the ingress channel. The exiting proton thus opens the seat for the next proton to join the ride. Children would likely become ill on the ATP synthase merry-go-round because it can spin at 7,800 revolutions per minute [199].

The rotating driveshaft interacts with a catalytic head that does not rotate. Picture a roof over the merry-go-round, not connected to the rotating merry-go-round but held stationary in place by a post on the side that is mounted to the ground. In ATP synthase, this post is the stator stalk, peripheral stalk, or *b*-subunit. The portions of the driveshaft that rotate near the stationary catalytic head result in conformational changes that combine adenosine diphosphate (ADP) and phosphate into adenosine triphosphate (ATP). The electric motor completes one complete rotation for every ten protons that pass from the high-proton-concentration side of the membrane to the low-concentration side of the membrane. Each complete rotation of ATP synthase generates three ATP molecules, which then serve as a universal "battery" for life.

In prokaryotes, the motor can even work in reverse, draining the energy from ATP to produce a proton gradient [200].

Having described the complete process of chemiosmotic coupling, we can now step back for a moment to look at the big picture. Chemiosmotic coupling requires a minimum of forty-five complex, interdependent protein molecules in the simplest forms of life. This is an oversimplification because we have not considered any of the proteins needed to produce these proteins, such as ribosomal proteins and transcription proteins. We have also not described the subsequent use of ATP; what good is ATP if there are no molecular machines to use it? All of the molecular machines that are powered by ATP must include a means for extracting the energy from ATP. Clearly, abiogenesis has a lot of explaining to do when it comes to energy harnessing and storage.

The Narrative of First Energy Harnessing

Nick Lane admits that "the evolution of chemiosmotic coupling is a mystery. The fact that all life is chemiosmotic implies that chemiosmotic coupling arose very early indeed in evolution" ([64], 83). Although the experts are willing to admit that the evolution of chemiosmotic coupling is a mystery, they can't help but provide a hypothesis of how it might have happened. Each such hypothesis is more of a hopeful narrative because, again, nobody knows the conditions of Earth when abiogenesis supposedly occurred. Therefore science, even prospective investigations in a controlled lab, can offer no real confidence as to what actually might have happened. Lane proposes that a primordial predecessor to the acetyl-CoA pathway, an energy-harnessing pathway used today by methanogens (in archaea) and acetogens (in bacteria), fueled reactions in hydrothermal vents. The acetyl-CoA pathway pumps protons across a membrane without the respiratory complexes—i.e., without the electron transport chain. However, the acetyl-CoA pathway still requires a set of complex enzymes to generate the proton gradient—enzymes that happen to be significantly different between methanogens and acetogens—and acetyl-CoA still requires the incredible complexity of ATP synthase to convert the proton gradient into ATP. To sidestep this complexity, Lane's imagination (in the absence of evidence) proposes the existence of a simpler primordial pathway based upon acetyl phosphate (to take the place of ATP, thus avoiding the need for ATP synthase) and methyl acetate (to take the place of acetyl-CoA in order to avoid the complexity of coenzyme A).

Advancing from this imaginary pathway of harnessing energy to the extraordinarily complex world of chemiosmotic coupling is then brushed away with a stroke: "The standard mechanisms of evolution eventually produced the sophisticated proteins in early cells, including ribosomes and the ATP synthase, proteins conserved universally across life today" ([64], 135). Here, we see a technical form of a "punt," calling upon the mystical powers of evolution to bridge the enormous gap between a hypothetical primordial means of energy harnessing and chemiosmotic coupling. Let's not forget that the "standard mechanisms of evolution" rely on random mutations and natural selection, so the steps along the hypothetical evolutionary pathway to arrive at a minimum of forty-five interacting proteins must convey a selective advantage—not only maintaining the ability to harness energy but to do it appreciably better than the hypothetical preceding method.

In contrast, Franklin Harold, author of *In Search of Cell History* and a devoted supporter of abiogenesis, claims that it is easier to exclude unlikely pathways to energy harnessing than to support a favorite. He begins by tossing methanogens under the bus because their method of energy production (the acetyl-CoA pathway) is found so rarely in extant life: "It is surely more parsimonious to consider methanogenesis as a latter invention of the *Euryarchaeota* and to exclude it from LUCA's repertoire" ([99], 76). Here, *Euryarchaeota* is a phylum of Archaea that includes the methanogens, and LUCA stands for the last universal common ancestor to all of life. In his mind, the acetyl-CoA pathway could at best serve as a "model for primordial bioenergetics," although this pathway "is anything but simple (even if one ignores the source of the complex cofactors) and is unlikely to represent the first biological economy" ([99], 76).

Thus, a prebiotic means to arrive at the requisite energy harnessing of life remains an enigma. Living organisms rely on a process with extraordinary complexity. Only a vivid imagination combined with reliance on the mystical powers of chemical evolution can hypothesize a prebiotic explanation, an explanation that cannot be approached by the familiar scientific methods that produce high confidence (e.g., repeated results, prospective study, and direct measurements).

Chapter 17

Interdependency of DNA, RNA, and Proteins

Assuming that all ten previous steps on the Stairway to Life have been achieved by purely natural processes, we now have genes that code for metabolic functions, reproduce themselves, and are accompanied by repair and regulatory mechanisms. However, all of this is embodied in RNA. The code contained in this RNA directly specifies the proper sequence of nucleotides for RNA to function as ribozymes. In other words, this RNA operates both as the genotype (the storage of information) and the phenotype (the information processing or metabolic activities). This is an imaginary scenario for life because no known life today can operate exclusively on ribozymes.[43]

The most recent and extensive study of the minimal requirements for life (i.e., an autonomously reproducing minimal version of *Synthia*) includes 493 genes [201]. Ribozymes certainly can perform some metabolic activities, but they do not have the versatility of protein enzymes; therefore, RNA alone has no hope of

---

43. Many viruses contain information only in the form of RNA. However, their lifecycle requires the assistance of a host cell's DNA and molecular machinery, and viruses are generally not classified as "living."

performing all of the minimal tasks of any known autonomously reproducing cell.

Transitioning Information Storage from RNA to DNA

All known life has distinct information-storage molecules and information-processing molecules, where the task of information storage generally occurs in DNA and the task of information processing generally occurs via proteins. Thus, we must explain the transition from our scenario of combined information storage and information processing in RNA to separate information storage and information processing in DNA and proteins.

However, the sequence of nucleotides that makes a functional RNA ribozyme (i.e., the information content in an RNA-based life scenario) has no correspondence to the sequence of amino acids that make a protein enzyme with similar function. This point requires some emphasis. In climbing the Stairway to Life up to this point, a large quantity of information has been accumulated in the form of RNA molecules: ribozymes composed of the four nucleotides A, U, G, and C, which directly facilitate chemical reactions. But there is no means of translating the information that codes for an RNA ribozyme into information that codes for a protein that performs the same function. Although all known life makes use of codons to translate RNA *code* into protein *code* (i.e., three nucleotides translate to one amino acid), there is no known means of translating an RNA *function* into a protein *function*. Every protein that has been identified throughout life is encoded in a mRNA, yet not a single mRNA behaves like its corresponding protein.

To use a simple hypothetical example, imagine that a ribozyme with a specific sequence of RNA like "AGUCUCGAAAGUAG" performs a function such as bonding a nitrogenous base and a ribose to make a nucleoside. Now imagine that a protein enzyme can perform the same function as this ribozyme. Knowing the functional RNA sequence "AGUCUCGAAAGUAG" tells us exactly nothing about the appropriate amino acid sequence needed to make a protein enzyme with a similar function. The transition from a hypothetical RNA-based metabolism to our familiar protein-based metabolism has no solution. Therefore, most of the information accumulated thus far in the Stairway to Life is a dead end. **Progressing from our hypothetical RNA-based life to arrive at the central dogma of molecular biology (i.e., the residue-by-residue transfer of sequential information from DNA to RNA to protein) requires more than just additional innovation; it requires starting over with different information, combined with the arrival of new molecular machinery for processing the information.**

Even if a miracle converted the code sequences for functional RNA molecules into DNA that codes for proteins with similar functions, we would still be no closer to life because this new DNA information has no value unless it can be reproduced and unless the information can be decoded and converted into functional proteins. Just as the DNA produced by Venter's team (the *Synthia* genome) could not constitute life on its own, information stored in DNA serves no purpose until it is accompanied by a large cohort of supporting molecules.

Reproduction of DNA, even in the simplest prokaryotes, requires the coordinated efforts of at least fourteen enzymes (including twenty-five polypeptides) and RNA to act as primers [134]. A simplified view of the minimal DNA replication process is provided in Figure 16. To highlight an interesting detail in Figure 16, the process of DNA replication in prokaryotes results in two interlocking rings of duplicated DNA. If the two rings cannot be separated, reproduction cannot proceed. In an old, familiar magic trick, the magician separates metal rings that are interlocked like links in a chain. In *E. coli*, a protein enzyme known as topoisomerase IV acts as the magician,[44] temporarily breaking one double helix of DNA, passing the other double helix through, then recombining the broken double helix [202]. Topoisomerase IV in *E. coli* consists of two different proteins made of 752 and 630 amino acids, respectively. Loss-of-function mutations of either protein are lethal to *E. coli* [203, 204]. If you've ever taken the antibiotic ciprofloxacin, you've proven that inhibition of topoisomerase IV kills bacteria ([205], 132).

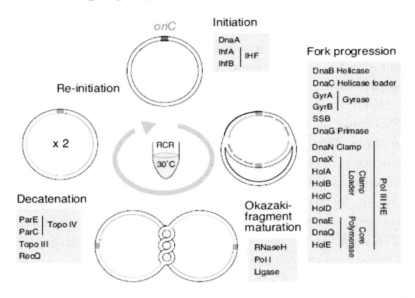

Figure 16. The minimal set of fourteen enzymes (twenty-five polypeptides) required to replicate the circular DNA in *E. coli*, starting from the top and progressing clockwise [134].

---

44. The interlocked molecules are known as catenanes, and topoisomerase IV performs decatenation, which sounds like an aspirational goal for dogs.

Summarizing thus far, the transition from RNA-based metabolic activities to the only life that we observe today would require entirely different information: DNA coding of amino acid sequences for functional proteins. The hypothesis that RNA molecules accumulated information toward a first living organism is a dead end because life as we know it today is based upon entirely different information. The source of this entirely different information in an abiotic world is unknown. In addition, reproduction of DNA requires a complex suite of proteins. These replication proteins are coded in the very DNA that they serve to reproduce. They are believed to have evolved through random mutations during DNA replication, followed by natural selection. However, DNA cannot be replicated without these proteins, the replication proteins cannot be produced without the DNA, and evolution cannot occur without replication. Thus, we have yet another series of impossible interdependencies for abiogenesis.

Layers of Impossible Interdependencies

Undeterred by conflicting requirements, we press on to the next requirement for life: the information encoded in the DNA requires additional machinery for decoding and production of proteins (i.e., the central dogma of molecular biology). As we summarized briefly in Chapter 3, decoding DNA and producing proteins starts with transcription into messenger RNA (mRNA), which requires the coordinated action of at least three essential components: a promoter region on the DNA for recognition of a gene, a transcription termination region of DNA, and transcription machinery (i.e., RNA polymerase, which is composed of five protein subunits in prokaryotes, including four unique kinds of proteins) that is very specific in recognizing the promoter and very accurate in transcribing the gene to mRNA. Of course, the production of RNA polymerase from the DNA that codes for RNA polymerase requires the action of RNA polymerase. Also, the DNA that codes for RNA polymerase cannot be reproduced without the replication proteins, but the replication proteins can only be produced from DNA with the help of RNA polymerase—yet another set of impossible interdependencies.

The next step is translation of the mRNA into a protein. In cells, accurate translation occurs via ribosomes. A prokaryote ribosome requires a combination of three complex ribosomal RNA molecules and more than forty-eight proteins, all properly folded and assembled in a hierarchical structure [206]. Notice that the components of a ribosome are encoded in DNA, and production of a ribosome itself requires translation of four dozen proteins, which can only happen via—you guessed it—a ribosome. Ribosomes are therefore essential to produce ribosomes. Further, the DNA that codes for ribosomes cannot be reproduced without the replication proteins, but the replication proteins can only be produced from DNA via ribosomes. Finally, the proteins in the ribosomes cannot be produced without RNA polymerase, and RNA polymerase cannot be produced without ribosomes—another set of impossible interdependencies.

A word formed by the letters *g*, *i*, *f*, and *t* carries a positive connotation according to the English translation, but those same four letters indicate poison according to the German translation. Similarly for a cell, proper translation of the mRNA code can spell the difference between life and death. Translation from mRNA to protein occurs via use of the genetic code to convert each set of three RNA nucleotides (i.e., a codon) into an amino acid. The genetic code and its accurate application are essential for life, but the arrival of the genetic code has no explanation. Francis Crick proposed the "frozen accident hypothesis," suggesting that the genetic code formed accidently, but, once formed, the genetic code could not change because such changes would be immediately lethal [207]. However, as mentioned in Chapter 3, the National Center for Biotechnology Information (NCBI) currently lists thirty-three different genetic code tables for a variety of life-forms [59]. For those who are interested, Eugene Koonin and Artem Novozhilov from the National Center for Biotechnology Information provide an excellent summary of three alternative theories for the arrival of the genetic code [208]. However, they summarize simply by stating: "None of the three major theories on the nature and evolution of the genetic code is unequivocally supported by the currently available data...Summarizing the state of the art in the study of the code evolution, we cannot escape considerable skepticism."

But there is a bigger problem. This too is well summarized by Koonin and Novozhilov:

> Any scenario of the code origin and evolution will remain vacuous if not combined with understanding of the origin of the coding principle itself and the translation system that embodies it. At the heart of this problem is a dreary vicious circle: what would be the selective force behind the evolution of the extremely complex translation system before there were functional proteins? And, of course, there could be no proteins without a sufficiently effective translation system. A variety of hypotheses have been proposed in attempts to break the circle but so far none of these seems to be sufficiently coherent or enjoys sufficient support to claim the status of a real theory ([208], 108).

In short, we observe many layers of fundamental interdependencies between the new molecular machinery that is required to reproduce DNA, to translate the code, and to manufacture proteins, and the required new DNA information to code for all these proteins. All of the conflicting requirements in this chapter arise from the essential interdependence between DNA, RNA, and proteins. DNA has no value without RNA and proteins, yet proteins are formed from DNA via the help of RNA and proteins. RNA is essential to produce proteins and for reproduction of DNA. Finally, RNA is necessary to produce proteins, but proteins modify RNAs via RNA splicing, RNA editing, RNA degradation, and RNA transport. Because DNA, RNA, and proteins are interdependent, they must all have appeared simultaneously to contribute to a living organism. The simultaneous arrival of such complex biopolymers with highly specific required interactions between the biopolymers presents quite a challenge for abiogenesis.

The Longer the DNA, the Longer the DNA

In addition, all these requirements on DNA make for a very lengthy DNA molecule, and maintenance of such a long molecule requires additional proteins that are coded in the DNA. An *E. coli* cell is about two micrometers long (two millionths of a meter) and one micrometer in diameter, and it contains a circular DNA molecule with 4.6 million base pairs. If fully extended, the DNA molecule would measure about 1.4 millimeters, or about 700 times longer than the *E. coli* cell [209]. Picture your car, representing an *E. coli*, containing a rope that represents the DNA. Scaling up the *E. coli* to become the size of your car (about five meters or sixteen feet in length), the DNA would correspondingly scale up to approximately 3.5 kilometers or 2.2 miles of rope with a diameter of six millimeters or ¼ inch, contained in your car. Figure 17 clarifies this comparison, showing an image of a gently isolated *E. coli* genomic DNA spread on an electron microscope grid and some intact *E. coli* cells with the same magnification. Indeed, all of that

DNA has to be compressed to fit within each bacterial cell. Now, imagine the *E. coli* cell duplicating this DNA before replication and needing to separate the two interlinked copies before cell division. Genomic DNAs are so long that they cannot fit into any cells without being highly compacted with the help of multiple proteins. For example, the DNA of *E. coli* is compacted by DNA-bridging proteins MukB, MukE, and MukF, as well as other proteins. Also, such a length of rope cannot be manipulated without kinking and supercoiling, especially when DNA is unwound for reproduction. Additional topoisomerase enzymes and structural maintenance of chromosome (SMC) proteins [210] are essential for this purpose. *E. coli* cells cannot survive at 37°C if any one of these proteins is absent ([211] and references therein). The more complex DNA becomes, the more complex it must become in order to remain functional.

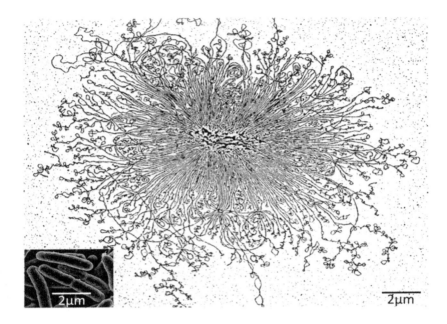

Figure 17. The highly convoluted *E. coli* genomic DNA. Imaged is a gently isolated *E. coli* nucleoid bound by cytochrome C, spread on an electron microscope grid, stained with uranyl acetate and visualized by transmission electron microscopy. The insert at the bottom left is part of a scanning electron micrograph of *E. coli* cells, grown in culture and affixed to a cover slip. One of the cells is outlined with a white line. The two images are presented at the same scale (2 μm). It is impossible for an *E. coli* cell to accommodate its genomic DNA unless the DNA is highly compacted, a task accomplished by DNA-binding proteins.

Chapter 18

Coordinated Cellular Purpose

On a warm summer weekend, a suburb dweller might find themselves set to the task of gardening. With shovel in hand, they aim to improve the landscape, desired plants flourishing in the desired locations and undesired plants removed and composted. Thrusting a shovel into the soil, they unintentionally cause near-Armageddon for a colony of ants. The ant colony, a product of countless hours of coordinated activities on a very small scale, lies in chaos and disarray. The organized tunnels and chambers are all destroyed. Eggs, larvae, pupae, and stored food are now exposed and scattered about. Feeling a touch of guilt yet unable to help the ants recover, the gardener pauses to observe the response of the ants. The initial flurry of chaotic activity eventually organizes into a coordinated effort to protect the queen, protect the eggs, and rebuild the tunnels and chambers. With a clear and singular purpose, and without an observable blueprint, the undaunted ants work tirelessly to build a new colony, restoring the organization, function, and homeostasis of the prior colony. The coordinated activity and the high-level organization follow from a tangible, inborn purpose.

Cells and ant colonies both consist of highly coordinated activities on small scales that are directed toward a clear purpose. This is the highest level of organization for an individual cell and the last step on the Stairway to Life. Assuming that all prior steps have been overcome by purely prebiotic processes over eons of time (an assumption that the prior eleven chapters incessantly invalidated), we now have ready access to all of the necessary ingredients for life. Our situation is similar to a petri dish that contains scrambled cellular contents—as if billions of bacteria were thoroughly blended, maintaining the integrity of the individual molecules but stripping them of their natural associations and organization in a living organism. We have complete genomes, rich with functional genes and regulatory components; complete proteins ready to make use of the DNA, drive reactions, extract energy, and build complex molecules; phospholipids with their ability to naturally form into bilayers and vesicles; and ample supplies of building materials and sources of energy. We have a very rich organic soup that seems to be just one step away from life. We prepare this soup carefully in a sterile environment and sit back and watch for life to start.

Under the right conditions, the phospholipids may spontaneously form vesicles composed of a single bilayer, each containing a random assortment of the soup's ingredients and perhaps fortuitously trapping a few random proteins within the bilayer. Under a microscope, this might begin to look like cells have formed—a hint of life. But life requires more than vesicles with random assortments of the proper contents. The cell membranes of living organisms serve as the setting for highly coordinated transfers of specific materials: food molecules enter, waste products exit, building materials enter, communicating molecules exit. In our petri dish, the membranes contain only occasional proteins that were haphazardly trapped during the spontaneous formation of vesicles. Many of these proteins are not intended to facilitate the entry or exit of materials, and half of those that are will be inverted, dutifully passing food out of the vesicle or toxins into the vesicle. The few transmembrane proteins that are intended to operate within the membrane and ended up in a proper orientation are inadequate to overcome the opposing forces and keep up with the demands of a living cell.

Inside the vesicles, enzymes are randomly at work—some breaking bonds, some creating bonds. The situation is like a construction project that must begin with demolition of the prior building, but both the demolition crew and the construction crew start to work at the same time. Endonucleases attack the DNA that could be used to provide order. Proteases break down useful proteins into small peptides. Some enzymes begin metabolizing the energy sources, yet they are not capable of organizing themselves cohesively as an assembly line associated with a closed membrane to sustain chemiosmotic coupling. Electrons are stripped from food sources, but free radicals result from improperly coordinated enzymatic activity, inflicting damage on neighboring molecules. Like a nuclear reactor without coordinated transfer of the energy from uranium atoms to electrical generators, the result is damage.

The DNA has a complete set of instructions for life, but the instructions are not being followed in proper order: Is it now time to replicate the instructions or to focus on obtaining food, to grow, to remove waste products, to hibernate, to attack invading DNA, or to divide into two cells? Portions of each of these activities are taking place randomly in various locations of the vesicle. Although each gene follows regulatory control, the regulatory signaling is chaotic, and anarchy exists at higher levels of regulation.

Beyond the genome, the epigenetics are also in chaos. For sixty years, biology textbooks have instructed students to focus on the central dogma of biology: the flow of information from DNA to RNA to proteins that forms the core of life. The reductionists had us believing that the central dogma of biology encompassed the entirety of the information content of life—that a complete understanding of the genes conferred a complete understanding of life. Increasingly, we now appreciate the importance of epigenetics: modifications of phenotype without a change in genotype. Epigenetics represent additional layers of cellular information. Again desiring simplification, we tend to view epigenetics as only modifying gene expression without changing the sequence of genes. But in the most general form, epigenetics speaks more broadly to the vast information contained in a living cell outside of the genome, including the higher-level organization, the homeostasis, the purpose.

Rudolf Virchow coined the phrase *Omnis cellula e cellula*—"every cell comes from a previous cell." In all known life, the daughter cells inherit not only DNA, RNA, proteins, energy sources, and building blocks, but they also inherit layers of organization, coordinated activity, and the purpose of the parent cell. The daughter cells naturally progress in a coordinated manner through the proper steps of growth and division, operating like fine-tuned machines, whereas the vesicles that randomly formed in the petri dish operate like an engine whose spark plugs fire at random intervals.

In this "bacteria-in-a-blender" scenario, we know that the result, every time, will be chaos and decay, not life [212]. Life is more than a soup of biomolecules. Life also requires the orchestrated operation of those molecules toward a unified purpose—the highest level of cellular organization and information content. Like an ant colony, life has an inborn purpose that coordinates all activity. This inborn purpose simply cannot be obtained by random arrangement and natural selection; it must be inherited from the parent cell. Life is not possible without it, and collections of molecules simply cannot evolve into it. The last insuperable step in the

Stairway to Life is the climax, the greatest challenge for a materialistic explanation.

Chapter 19

The View from the Top of the Stairway

One reason for climbing a stairway is to achieve a better view. Having ascended each of the steps in the Stairway to Life, we can now reflect on the overall stairway metaphor (Figure 6). The stairway metaphor conveniently served to break the overwhelming problem of abiogenesis into smaller required components so that each component could be discussed in turn. This was quite helpful for writing an organized book. However, the stairway metaphor has a serious limitation: it risks providing the false impression that small steps are easy to achieve, such that the overall challenge of abiogenesis may appear to be facilitated by the availability of sequential steps. Nothing could be further from the truth because in reality, a cliff is a far better metaphor than a stairway.

Ascending the Stairway in the prebiotic world was expected to take time—geologic time. However, simple thermodynamics ensures the degradation of biomolecules over time unless a precisely directed application of energy can overcome the degradation. To achieve this, each new biomolecule must be paired immediately with a novel and precise mechanism that applies energy to either repair or replace the biomolecule. Similarly, information-storage molecules like DNA provide no progress toward life unless other molecules decode the information into an action and reproduce the DNA. This requires simultaneous arrival of the information, the decoding process, and the machinery to replicate the information. Finally, without a semipermeable barrier, the essential components for life would diffuse apart, and a predominance of undesirable molecules would interfere with essential reactions. The semipermeable barrier requires the simultaneous arrival of phospholipids and proteins, which requires the simultaneous arrival of the information and decoding process. Therefore, information, the utilization of information, the replication of information, the precise application of energy, and a suitable containment structure must all appear simultaneously to initiate life. The stairway depicted in Figure 6 is intentionally steep but not sufficiently steep to convey the temporal constraints required to start life. Proper conversion of the Stairway into a cliff imposes additional unachievable requirements on abiogenesis and a harsh reality check for those who support it.

Opportunities to Stack the Deck

Sensing the sheer improbability of abiogenesis, those who are committed to naturalistic explanations for the start of life sometimes look to the stars. If the size of planet Earth and a span of less than one billion years (the hypothesized duration from Earth's formation to the appearance of first life) is insufficient for the spontaneous generation of life, odds are increased when the entire universe and all time since the Big Bang are considered to be "in scope." A recent review article authored by thirty-three scientists and scholars from the physical and biological sciences summarized this thinking:

The transformation of an ensemble of appropriately chosen biological monomers (e.g. amino acids, nucleotides) into a primitive living cell capable of further evolution appears to require overcoming an information hurdle of superastronomical proportions, an event that could not have happened within the time frame of the Earth except, we believe, as a miracle. All laboratory experiments attempting to simulate such an event have so far led to dismal failure. It would thus seem reasonable to go to the biggest available "venue" in relation to space and time. A cosmological origin of life thus appears plausible and overwhelmingly likely to us [213].

The same logic led Francis Crick, discoverer of the structure of DNA, to adopt panspermia, the science-fiction approach to starting life elsewhere in the universe when nonmaterialistic explanations cannot be tolerated. Yet panspermia and all of time since the Big Bang do not have the power to redeem abiogenesis. Adding several billion more years—the time since the beginning of the universe, rather than the time available on Earth—is but a rounding error against the likelihood of producing life by chance. Furthermore, as we have already discussed, climbing the Stairway (or, more accurately, ascending the cliff) needs to be achieved very rapidly, so additional time is not the answer. And regardless of where life started in the universe, each step in the Stairway to Life still applies. We know that life exists on Earth, so believing that life did not start on Earth only complicates matters further by adding one more step to the Stairway: transportation to Earth.

Recognizing that even the inclusion of all planets in the known universe and all time since the Big Bang may be insufficient to overcome the odds of abiogenesis, the next level of desperation to support abiogenesis is to imagine a multiverse. If our universe is just one of an infinite number of universes, the impossible seemingly becomes possible and the possible becomes certain. Life may exist only in our universe and only on planet Earth, so out of the infinite possible locations, only we had the good fortune of overcoming the odds of abiogenesis. Unfortunately, there is no empirical evidence that a multiverse exists, nor can it be falsified. Therefore, belief in a multiverse relies heavily upon faith and minimally upon science.

A View of Venter's Work from the Top

Coming full circle, we can now review Venter's efforts to create a synthetic cell from the perspective of the Stairway to Life. Venter ascended the Stairway by stacking the deck in his favor, by borrowing from existing life, and by injecting human intelligence along the way (see Table 2).

Venter skipped the first two steps (formation and concentration of building blocks and homochirality of building blocks) by purchasing purified homochiral nucleotides that were produced with the help of living organisms and by borrowing the other building blocks from existing life (*Capri*). Venter overcame the paradox of water via carefully designed reactions that used selectively activated and inactivated reagents that are synthesized, stored, and used in an anhydrous and inert atmosphere [53, 54]. To produce homolinked oligos, Venter employed complex synthetic recipes with pure reagents, separation processes, and carefully controlled conditions to block unwanted chemical bonding and to increase the probability of the desired bonding arrangement. Even under these conditions, the oligos were constrained to a length of sixty-five to one hundred base pairs because each newly added base pair had a small probability of forming an incorrect bond, and none of the reactions had a yield of 100%. To increase the length of the synthesized DNA, Venter had to borrow the molecular machinery of living organisms—machinery that already had perfect homochirality and homolinkage—and conscripted living cells to manufacture DNA. The reproduction of biopolymers in Venter's work was all conducted by intact living cells or the machinery borrowed from living cells. The genes, the regulatory mechanisms, and the biopolymer repair mechanisms of *Synthia* were entirely borrowed from *Myco* and *Capri*. The membrane- and energy-harnessing machinery of *Synthia* was inherited from *Capri*, but over time it was replaced by *Synthia* through the use of its own genome. The DNA donor *Myco* and the recipient cell *Capri* initially met the interdependency requirements of DNA, RNA, and proteins, but these were eventually all replaced by molecules produced from the *Synthia* genome. Finally, the host cell *Capri* and the *Myco*-based genome provided the coordinated cellular purpose that was inherited by *Synthia*. Perhaps Venter's bold summary of *Synthia*—"the first self-replicating species that we've had on the planet whose parent is a computer"—could have benefited from a proper acknowledgment of the genius of life itself.

Table 2: Venter's ascent of the Stairway to Life

Step	Chemistry	Biology	Venter's Solution
Formation of building blocks	Mixture of a nearly infinite variety of molecules	• 20 amino acids • 5 nucleotides	• Purchase purified reagents • Borrow from existing cells
Homochirality	• D- and L-amino acids • 8 chiral forms of each DNA nucleotide • 16 chiral forms of each RNA nucleotide	• Homochiral amino acids • Homochiral nucleotides	• Purchase purified reagents • Borrow from existing cells
Paradox of water	Strong preference for breaking bonds within biomolecules	Highly specific applications of energy (via enzymes) to drive polymerization reactions	• Use of modified reagents made, stored, and used under anhydrous conditions • Use of dehydrating agents • Conscription of molecular machinery from living organisms
Homolinkage	Chaotic bonding results in "asphalt"	Highly specific applications of energy (via enzymes) constrain polymerization reactions to a preferred linkage	• Controlled conditions, complex synthetic recipes, and separation processes • Conscription of molecular machinery from living organisms
Biopolymer reproduction	Never observed	Conducted by molecular nanomachines	Conscription of molecular machinery from living organisms
Nucleotide sequences forming useful code	Infinitesimal chance of obtaining any useful code by random arrangement	Codes inherited from parent cells	Borrowed codes from existing life
Means of gene regulation	Unapproachable from chemistry	Inherited from parent cells	Borrowed from existing life
Means for repairing biopolymers	Unapproachable from chemistry	Inherited from parent cells	Borrowed from existing life
Selectively permeable membranes	Unapproachable from chemistry	Inherited from parent cells	Borrowed from existing life
Means of harnessing energy	Unapproachable from chemistry	Inherited from parent cells	Borrowed from existing life
Interdependency of DNA, RNA, and proteins	Unapproachable from chemistry	Inherited from parent cells	Borrowed from existing life
Coordinated cellular purpose	Unapproachable from chemistry	Inherited from parent cells	Borrowed from existing life

For most aspects of biology, the assumption of methodological naturalism is uncontested. One example is studying the impact of a chemotherapy drug on cancer in mice. However, it is possible to imagine scenarios where the assumption of methodological naturalism could be—we repeat, *could be*—less certain. Imagine that we wish to study the impact of a new experimental drug on the progression of cancer in children. We enroll two thousand children who have been diagnosed with cancer into a clinical study: one thousand will receive the experimental drug, and one thousand will receive the current standard-of-care treatment. Under the assumption of methodological naturalism, the survival rate of these patients over time should indicate if the drug is having a positive impact.

Unlike conducting the trial on mice, cancer in children creates great emotional distress, prompting the family and friends of the patients to seek out any possible cure. Those with even the slightest vestige of religious faith will be pleading daily for supernatural intervention. Imagine that each of the one thousand patients who receives the experimental drug also has a strong faith in God and has a family and friends with strong faith who pray daily for healing, whereas the one thousand patients who receive current standard-of-care treatment do not. Is it possible that the results of the clinical study may not reflect the true benefit of the experimental drug but could be tainted by supernatural intervention? In other words, should the assumption of methodological naturalism be questioned here? Any atheist would surely disagree because they have cemented the assumption of methodological naturalism in their minds. Atheists have gone one step further by adopting philosophical naturalism (also known as metaphysical naturalism or ontological naturalism), the belief that there are no supernatural forces at all, ever. For the atheist, questioning the assumption of methodological naturalism is like questioning the force of gravity; it is essential and foundational to their worldview. But for those who believe that supernatural activity is possible, our hypothetical study of an experimental cancer drug in children should instill some uncertainty about the assumption of methodological naturalism.[45]

Next, we take the assumption of methodological naturalism to its extreme: origin-of-life research. Here, the atheist remains confident in the assumption of methodological naturalism, firmly stating that science is the only way to understand origins, perhaps even believing that science is the only way to obtain knowledge (known as scientism), and that the practice of science requires us to first exclude the possibility of supernatural intervention. To the atheist, the assumption of methodological naturalism is equally trivial when applied to the study of origins or the study of boiling liquids; it is so trivial that it deserves no mention.

Yet in the study of origins, the assumption of methodological naturalism immediately excludes possible explanations, instilling a profound bias. If a scientific approach to origins first assumes that God and any other form of intelligence had no role, then interpretations of evidence will always be biased toward supporting a natural origin—there simply is no alternative. Thus, scientific evidence suggests that life originated by a natural process because anything outside of natural processes is excluded a priori by definition. If science is the only way to understand origins, and any "scientific" explanation for origins must exclude God a priori, then the application of science must lead us away from God, thus extending methodological naturalism to philosophical naturalism,

---

45. Fortunately, in a real clinical trial of this nature, subjects would be randomly assigned to the experimental group or to the control group. This randomization is a way of removing bias, such as the possible bias from prayer. In an actual study, because of randomization, it is much more likely that the two groups of patients would contain equal distributions of people of faith and people with no faith.

otherwise known as atheism. This line of thinking had a profound influence on the upbringing and early career of one of the authors (CT).

These consequences follow from the initial assumption of methodological naturalism. If this assumption could be validated, we could obtain clarity. For study of the origin of life, validating the assumption of methodological naturalism is akin to accepting philosophical naturalism, for if supernatural powers had nothing to do with the origin of life, they likely have no role in the universe. Yet how could such an assumption be validated? The scientific method cannot help; it can only beg the question. Should we trust human logic? The authority of scientists? Democratic vote? The assumption of methodological naturalism can neither be validated nor invalidated. Blind acceptance without acknowledgement of the assumption of methodological naturalism is a major contributor to belief in abiogenesis and a major contributor to the circular conclusion that science supports abiogenesis.

Public Schools Encourage Belief in Abiogenesis

Public schools, wishing to avoid controversy and succumbing to pressure from groups like the National Center for Science Education, the American Civil Liberties Union (ACLU), and Americans United for Separation of Church and State, only present evidence in a manner that encourages the adoption of abiogenesis (see the quotes from biology textbooks in the introduction). The message of the Stairway to Life, a rather discouraging message for abiogenesis, is essentially censored from public school biology textbooks. In seeking to avoid infringing upon the Establishment Clause of the First Amendment, public schools are, perhaps unknowingly, promoting philosophical naturalism and unnecessarily creating a conflict between science and religion in the minds of students. If a biology textbook says, "Life arose from nonlife via chemical evolution," ([13], 3) a student with almost any religious background will immediately be conflicted: either science is wrong or religion is wrong. If the student concludes that science is wrong, the student may lose trust in other scientific results and turn away from studying science. Conversely, if the student concludes that their religion is wrong, schools may be violating the Free Exercise Clause of the First Amendment.[46]

Neo-Darwinian Evolution Makes Abiogenesis Look Easy

According to the grand scope of evolution, all life on Earth evolved from a common ancestor, a single cell. The commonly held view portrays this universal common ancestor as a very simple organism. The prevailing belief therefore credits purely natural processes for the complexification of life from a rudimentary cell to the arrival of human beings. This line of thinking then proceeds: if purely natural processes can accomplish such a monumental task, producing the first living organism from prebiotic molecules should be easy. In other words, the stunning success of biological evolution implies chemical evolution.

As summarized in the preceding chapters, the simplest known autonomously reproducing life-form requires more than four hundred genes, approximately 500,000 base pairs of DNA, and many interdependent complex biological molecules, all organized in hierarchical layers of great complexity. Claims of simpler "proto-cells" remain within the domain of imagination. As explained through the Stairway to Life, all observable evidence provides no hope that natural processes can produce life. To highlight one fundamental

---

46. The complete First Amendment to the Constitution of the United States of America states: "Congress shall make no law respecting an establishment of religion, or prohibiting the free exercise thereof." The Free Exercise Clause is the second half, stating that government cannot manifest hostility to a religion.

step, chemical evolution cannot occur without replicators, but self-replicating molecules have never been observed.[47] Therefore, the acceptance of biological evolution, even in its grandest manifestation, contributes nothing in support of chemical evolution.

Rejection of Theism

Undoubtedly, some claim to be atheists with little contemplation of what such a belief implies; they just don't like the alternative. Specifically, the problem of the origin of first life may never concern them, or, in an effort to justify their atheism, they eagerly adopt any interpretation that favors abiogenesis. They may express their belief as, "We are here, so life must have started on its own." The assumption of methodological naturalism remains their close ally, providing a false sense of security that they stand on the higher scientific ground. While there are certainly a wide variety of reasons for rejecting theism, humans tend to resist authority and accountability to a higher power. Theism places all humans in a position of subordination to God, which is intolerable for those who would like to think that they are the source of authority, accountable to no one.

The well-known American philosopher Thomas Nagel explained his atheism as a "fear of religion":

> I am talking about something much deeper—namely, the fear of religion itself. I speak from experience, being strongly subject to this fear myself: I want atheism to be true and am made uneasy by the fact that some of the most intelligent and well-informed people I know are religious believers. It

---

47. As explained in Chapter 11, although DNA is often described as self-replicating, DNA replication requires a large array of complex supporting molecules.

isn't just that I don't believe in God and, naturally, hope that I'm right in my belief. It's that I hope there is no God! I don't want there to be a God; I don't want the universe to be like that [216].

Desire for a godless universe may encourage belief in abiogenesis but only by allowing bias to suppress the reality depicted by the Stairway to Life.

God Would Not Allow Suffering

Finally, many who have experienced great hardship cannot understand how a God who cares for us would allow suffering to happen. They choose to resolve the apparent conflict by concluding that there must not be a God. As a result, any scientific support for a naturalistic origin of life (abiogenesis and grand evolution) will be embraced to rationalize their belief and resolve their inner conflict.

Alternative resolutions to this conflict that are parsimonious with the existence of God are certainly beyond the scope of this book. Many great resources exist on the topic, such as *The Problem of Pain* by C. S. Lewis.

if the foundational assumption of methodological naturalism is incorrect, then science has no hope of correcting itself. Misreading a compass can lead one down the wrong path, but the problem can be corrected by improved use of the compass. However, if the compass is fundamentally pointing in the wrong direction and we either are unaware of the foundational flaw or if we insist on using the compass even though we know it is flawed, no improvement in compass-reading skills will get us back on the right path.

A second problem with this new view of biology also follows from the assumption of methodological naturalism. Abiogenesis is the only acceptable origin-of-life hypothesis, given methodological naturalism. Yet the available evidence to support abiogenesis is abysmal. Those who endorse abiogenesis must therefore resort to narrative in the absence of relevant evidence. The narrative includes a generous serving of imaginary entities to fill the numerous prebiotic gaps. If nucleotides can't be produced abiotically, they imagine that life began with proto-nucleotides. If self-replicating molecules happen to be unobservable, they can still imagine chemical evolution working to increase molecular complexity over time. If enzymes can't be produced abiotically, they imagine that proto-enzymes got things started. If functional membranes can't be formed abiotically, proto-membranes should do the trick. If cells can't form abiotically, certainly proto-cells could help. Here, the strict materialists find themselves in the awkward position of relying upon unobservable, imaginary entities as the foundation for their own existence.

The narrative also includes a wide variety of materialistic hypotheses for abiogenesis. Maybe the first biopolymers were organized by clay minerals. Maybe the extreme temperature and acidity of "black smokers" or "white smokers" started life. Perhaps it was the alkaline, nonsmoker hydrothermal vents. Biology textbooks continue to prefer lightning strikes in a reducing atmosphere, but maybe it was a neutral atmosphere. Life may have started with RNA or with small catalytic molecules that initiated metabolic reactions. Maybe RNA collaborated with peptides or other small molecules. Maybe life started as viruses or as membranes. Life may have come from outer space, or the molecules for life may have arrived on meteors.

If none of these hypotheses bear fruit, maybe undiscovered laws of physics make life unavoidable. In his 1944 book, *What Is Life?*, Erwin Schrödinger conceded that "living matter, while not eluding the 'laws of physics' as established up to date, is likely to involve 'other laws of physics' hitherto unknown" [218]. Other physicists have carved a space for abiogenesis by proposing "constructor theory," basically stating that nothing is impossible unless a law of physics explicitly forbids it [219]. Paul Davies, a prominent physicist at Arizona State University, concluded:

> People often say that the probability of life forming by chance is so low there must have been intelligent design or a miracle. I find that anathema. Religious people have got to move on and get away from the idea that there's a superbeing who fits it all up. What I find more congenial and much more intellectually respectable is the notion of fundamental laws of organisation that turn matter into life—a life principle built into the laws of the universe [220].

But he then conceded: "It is wishful thinking because at this stage I can't demonstrate it" [220]. These undisclosed new laws of physics strangely provide a taste of the élan vital of vitalism, and the wide variety of hypotheses for abiogenesis dramatically underscores the paucity of evidence that supports the concept.

This mélange of imaginary entities and hypotheses, mere shots in the dark, born of desperation, expose a fundamental hypocrisy. **Arguing that an unfalsifiable, unscientific, unobservable being had no role in the start of life, scientists replace this being with entities and hypotheses that are themselves unfalsifiable, unscientific and unobservable.**

Study of the origin of life under the assumption of methodological naturalism is akin to philosophical naturalism and is clearly problematic. If we maintain the current approach to abiogenesis, clinging to methodological naturalism and claiming that the evidence for abiogenesis is compelling, we can predict one of two possible outcomes: 1) the world could be convinced to accept abiogenesis, but abiogenesis could be a fallacy that we accepted because our practice of science deceived us, or 2) the world could reject abiogenesis despite strong support from the scientific community, which could substantially erode public confidence in science. Clearly, neither outcome is desirable.

Alternatively, the origin of life could be studied without the constraints imposed by methodological naturalism. This would free science to pursue the truth wherever the evidence leads. The Stairway to Life specifies a set of requirements to start life, to overcome the extraordinary impasse between chemistry and biology. Failure to meet any of the requirements should be grounds for rejecting abiogenesis. In the nearly one hundred years since the Russian chemist Alexander Oparin and British scientist J. B. S. Haldane first ignited interest in abiogenesis, our appreciation for the requirements to start life has grown immensely. For example, Oparin and Haldane likely did not know that the simplest forms of life require approximately four hundred genes; that homochirality, gene regulation, and DNA repair mechanisms are essential for life; or that RNA, DNA, and proteins are entirely interdependent in life. The number of known requirements to start life has clearly grown faster than our ability to meet the requirements through prebiotic laboratory synthesis. Out of relative ignorance, Oparin and Haldane may have been justified in their optimism about abiogenesis. Today, we should know better. Abiogenesis is losing ground. The Stairway to Life is not a static set of requirements; it represents a snapshot in time of the growing impasse between chemistry and biology—a trend that will certainly continue as we learn more about life.

Life may not depend upon special atoms, special chemical bonds, or an élan vital. But life does contain something quite special: layers upon layers of information in a hierarchy of molecular organization that simply cannot be produced abiotically. As noted by Sara Walker and Paul Davies:

> Although it is notoriously hard to identify precisely what makes life so distinctive and remarkable, there is general agreement that its informational aspect is one key property, and perhaps the key property. The manner in which information flows through and between cells and sub-cellular structures is quite unlike anything else observed in nature. If life is more than just complex chemistry, its unique informational management properties may be the crucial indicator of this distinction, which raises the all-important question of how the informational properties characteristic of living systems arose in the first place [221].

The only known source for this type of information[48] is intelligence. Living organisms and the Stairway to Life are powerful evidence of God—an inescapable conclusion when one is free to follow the evidence wherever it leads.

---

48. Sara Walker and Paul Davies distinguish the information found in living organisms from trivial forms of information like crystals (think of a snowflake) or layers of sediment because the information in living organisms has direct causal efficacy over the matter it is instantiated in [221].

Epilogue

I didn't know, Judge,
That what I did was against the law.
I just said what I saw.

—Harve Zemach [222]

In my laboratory course for students who are not biology majors, I (CT) started by describing the methods of biological sciences. Students were taught about assumption and inference, hypothesis and experiment, interpolation and extrapolation. The students were warned that extrapolation, which estimates an unmeasured quantity by extending a line (or a conclusion) beyond the measured/observed data range, is much less certain than interpolation, which estimates an unmeasured quantity based on the trend shown by data points scattering on both sides of the unmeasured quantity, and thus extrapolation should be used only in very special circumstances, with caution.

One of the exercises on experimental design and interpretation was a computer simulation of Francesco Redi's experiment on spontaneous generation [2]. In the first experiment, six jars were divided into two groups, one group with open mouths and the other with closed lids. Snake carcasses were placed into each of the jars. The carcasses in the jars with open mouths became covered with maggots because flies laid eggs on the carcasses, while the carcasses in the jars with lids did not grow maggots. All students concluded that the experiment proved that spontaneous generation was impossible—i.e., living things could not be formed from nonliving materials. The students were then provided with an objection to their conclusion: the lids on the jars prevented air from entering, and maggots did not form in the second set of jars because air is essential for life. Therefore, this experiment did not suggest that spontaneous generation was impossible. To address this objection, gauze was used instead of lids in a follow-up experiment. As Redi predicted, based on his theory that adult flies laid eggs on the meat, and the eggs turned into maggots, no maggots were formed in the meat in the jars covered with gauze. All students agreed that the second experiment proved that spontaneous generation was impossible.

"However, the meat eventually became rotten, right?" I said. "Even food kept in refrigerators turns bad, right? So Redi's experiments only proved that animals like flies could not be generated spontaneously, while it remained possible that microorganisms could be generated spontaneously."

All students nodded.

At this point, I introduced Louis Pasteur's pasteurization experiment, which convinced the world that even microorganisms could not be generated spontaneously.

And all students agreed on that conclusion. The following text is a record of my conversation with my students afterward.

TAN. Are you confident that the experiments by Redi and Pasteur have proved that spontaneous generation is impossible?

STUDENTS. Yes.

TAN. Sure?

STUDENTS. Yes.

TAN. Does it matter what sizes the jars/bottles were?

STUDENTS. No.

TAN. Does it matter how long they waited?

STUDENTS. No.

TAN. Sure?

STUDENTS. Yes.

TAN. What if the bottles are very big? I mean very big, really big. Still positive?

STUDENTS. Yes.

TAN. How about this big? (*A picture of the globe was shown.*) Still positive?

STUDENTS. Uh… (*Some hesitated.*)

TAN. How about this big? (*A picture of the visible universe of the Hubble deep field was shown.*) Still positive?

STUDENTS. (*Silence.*)

How about you?

We have a great quantity of evidence to refute the concept of spontaneous generation, such as the experiments of Redi and Pasteur, and the entire contents of this book. However, our confidence quickly diminishes when we extrapolate the conclusion to include the whole Earth or the whole universe in their whole history.

We do not have any evidence of spontaneous generation, except those erroneous observations disproved by the experiments of Redi and Pasteur. However, our society as a whole, without any observational basis, has become very confident that life did arise spontaneously from nonlife four billion years ago. Anyone who dares to question is quickly labeled as "a creationist," or "not scientific," risking their career and ability to obtain funding or to publish in mainstream journals.

To return to my class, I ended it with a discussion on logic and scientific reasoning. We specifically talked about two basic logical forms, *modus ponens* and *modus tollens*, and two common logical fallacies connected with them: the fallacy of affirming the consequent and the fallacy of denying the antecedent.

Modus ponens takes the following form:

If A, then B.

A is true, therefore B.

Modus tollens takes the following form:

If A, then B.

Not B, therefore not A.

The fallacy of affirming the consequent takes the following form:

If A, then B.

B is true, therefore A.

The fallacy of denying the antecedent takes the following form:

If A, then B.

Not A, therefore not B.

Example:

If it is snowing, then it is cold outside.

Valid reasoning:

- *It is snowing; therefore, it is cold outside. (Modus ponens)*

- *It is not cold outside; therefore, it is not snowing. (Modus tollens)*

Invalid reasoning:

- *It is cold outside; therefore, it is snowing. (Fallacy of affirming the consequent)*

- *It is not snowing; therefore, it is not cold outside. (Fallacy of denying the antecedent)*

If we replace "it is snowing"—the "A"—with "my theory is correct" and "it is cold outside"—the "B"—with "I will see these results," then we have the following:

If my theory is correct, then I will see these results.

Valid reasoning:

- *My theory is correct; therefore, I see these results. (Modus ponens)*

- *I do not see these results; therefore, my theory is not correct. (Modus tollens)*

Invalid reasoning:

- *I see these results; therefore, my theory is correct. (Fallacy of affirming the consequent)*

- *My theory is not correct; therefore, I do not see these results. (Fallacy of denying the antecedent)*

In other words, the belief that *if we see the results predicted by our theory, then we have proven our theory* is not reliable because of the fallacy of affirming the consequent. An observation that confirms our prediction only supports our theory, but it cannot prove it. Therefore, "If I see these results, then my theory *may* be true" is probably a true conditional proposition with respect to science, while "If I see these results, then I have proven my theory" is a false conditional statement.

Unfortunately, I, like my fellow scientists, do this kind of logically invalid reasoning all the time. We generate hypotheses or theories based on some observations, make predictions based on our theories, and perform experiments to prove or disprove our theories by checking if our experimental results match our predictions. If the results are as we predicted, we celebrate that our observations have proven our theory to be correct. Logically, the match of our results and our predictions only shows that our observations are consistent with our theory; they do not prove our theory to be correct. We can only conclude that as far as our observations go, our theory has not been proven wrong. Later experiments and observations may prove that our theory is wrong.

Such a scenario actually occurred in the seventeenth century regarding the spontaneous generation of life—the idea that life, at least primitive forms of life, constantly arises from inanimate matter. This idea was put forward most prominently by the great Greek philosopher Aristotle (384 BC–322 BC) and held for more than two thousand years until the nineteenth century [223, 224]. The long and widely held claim of Aristotle was supported by a wrongly interpreted experiment in the seventeenth century, showing that mice could be generated from piles of grain and sweaty clothing. Additional inappropriate support came from the common observation that maggots form from rotten animal flesh. This claim of spontaneous generation was disproven gradually with many carefully controlled experiments, especially those of Francesco Redi in the seventeenth century and those of Louis Pasteur in the nineteenth century.

One may wish to formulate the above argument about theory and experimental result this way:

If I see these results, then my theory is correct.

Valid reasoning:

I see these results; therefore, my theory is correct. (Modus ponens)

In other words, now we have a proper modus ponens, implying that if A is true, then B is true. If this is our argument, we can logically conclude that our theory is correct.

However, we have illustrated earlier that the truth of this conditional is problematic. It is not necessarily true that seeing certain results necessitates that our theory is correct. This can be further demonstrated by the following example:

If the Eskimo has only ever seen snow, rocks, and water, then the whole world is made of snow, rocks, and water.

The Eskimo has only ever seen snow, rocks, and water.

Therefore, the whole world is made of snow, rocks, and water.

This is a legitimate modus ponens. If the conditional is true, then the Eskimo who has only seen snow, rocks, and water proves deductively that the world is made of these three components. But obviously it is not true that the world is made entirely of these three things. Our if-then statement is false, and therefore our conclusion, although a perfectly legitimate logical deduction, is also false. This kind of reasoning is deductively valid but not sound. Otherwise, if we begin with what appears to be a reasonable statement—if we believe our conditional—then affirming the antecedent proves the consequent. If our conditional statement is false, we may be able to prove anything, even that the world is made of entirely of snow with a deductively legitimate argument.

Therefore, in objective reality, we can never prove that our theory is true. We can only disprove our theory. Practically speaking, even our ability to disprove our theories is also limited. For example, Redi's experiment leaves open the possibility that microorganisms can be generated spontaneously. And Pasteur's experiment leaves open the possibility that when his bottles are as big as the Earth or the universe, or if he has waited billions of years, or if there is supernatural intervention, spontaneous generation may be possible.

My point is that our observations or experiments are limited, that science is limited, that we humans are limited. It is incorrect for us to allow speculations and imagination concerning unobserved and unobservable phenomena to stand on equal footing with the results of controlled experiments that are repeatable and testable. If you could turn a reptile into a bird in the laboratory, it would not be proof that random variation and natural selection did the same thing a little less than two hundred million years ago. The Venter team, and supposedly any other person who could follow their protocol, can repeatedly turn a *Capri* cell into a *Myco* cell by transferring the *Myco* genomic DNA that contains the artificial antibiotic resistance transgene into *Capri* and then killing off the *Capri* cells that lack the antibiotic resistance transgene—changing one bacterial species into another [225]. This does not mean that was how the original *Myco* cells originated.

Venter's cloning experiment suggests that life could not have come about via natural processes, even if all the necessary nucleotides, lipids, and amino acids, or even a lot of pure DNAs, RNAs, or proteins—or a mixture of unrelated DNAs, RNAs, and proteins—were provided. It is necessary for a genomic DNA and its cognate RNAs and proteins to work together for any cell to function, remain alive, and replicate itself. Moreover, even all the hardware and the software of life, including a fully assembled genomic DNA and all its encoded RNAs and proteins, are still not enough to make a living cell, not even a simple bacterial cell. All observable evidence states that only a preexisting living cell can make another living cell.

It appears that the more we know about life at the molecular level, the more we lose hope for finding a natural, materialistic explanation for the origin of life.

Indeed, it is fundamentally important for us to know where we came from. However, it is even more important for us to know where we are going. If we don't know either, we will certainly make a mess of what lies in between.

Anticipated Objections

We anticipate that some of the statements and conclusions of this book will be objectionable to some readers. The following is an attempt to address some of the anticipated objections. To post a comment or question, please contact the authors at scientificevolution.com@gmail.com or visit www.scientificevolution.com.

Objection: Nearly 100,000 peer-reviewed scientific manuscripts have been published on abiogenesis. You have reviewed a very small fraction and have arrived at sweeping conclusions. The scientific literature is much more compelling than your interpretation.

Response: The current state of scientific literature on abiogenesis is the result of an extreme form of publication bias. Because of methodological naturalism, science is constrained to seek the best explanation for the origin of life that does not include God or any intelligent cause. Submitted manuscripts that suggest the need for a supernatural force or an intelligent designer are summarily rejected and the authors are persecuted. Also, journals have a well-known bias for publishing only positive results. As a result, scientific papers are almost exclusively encouraging when presenting materialistic explanations for the origin of life. Books like this one are therefore essential to provide balance and objectivity—to correct the extreme bias of the scientific literature.

Objection: Your argument is a plea to the "God of the gaps." Just because science doesn't have all the answers doesn't mean that we have to invoke God to fill the gaps.

Response: The entirety of this book seeks to provide a proper scope to the "gap." The Stairway to Life clarifies that the gap is not simply a missing puzzle piece or a set of unclear details. The gap is, in fact, the entirety of the origin of life. And the gap is growing over time as we learn more about the complexity of cells and as efforts to produce components of life via realistic prebiotic approaches fail.

As we have mentioned, additional steps will be added to the Stairway to Life over time. These steps will come from previously unexplored processes that are required for life. For example, we mentioned in Chapter 17 that the current best approximation of a minimal cell that can reproduce autonomously includes 493 genes [201]. This same report specifies that 91 of the 493 genes perform unknown functions. Therefore, about 20% of the minimal genome codes for functions that we have not yet explored. Further, the genome is not the only information contained in life. We are just beginning to explore other forms of information found in living organisms, such as the sugar code that encapsulates cells [226]. Future exploration in these areas will result in new steps in the Stairway to Life and an ever-increasing "gap." The emperor is not simply missing a lapel pin; the emperor has no clothes.

Our conclusion that creative intelligence was essential to start life is based on what we do know, not on what we don't know. The arguments in this book do not take the following form: "No one knows how life began; therefore, God did it." Rather, the inference to the need for intelligence in the origin of life follows directly from what we do know about the requirements for life and what we do know about chemistry, physics, thermodynamics, and biology. Turning this objection around, choosing to maintain a belief in abiogenesis despite the absence of a reasonable approach to the Stairway to Life is a "materialism-of-the-gaps" approach—i.e., "we don't know how life began, but we know that only natural processes were involved."

Objection: You claim in Chapter 21 that abiogenesis is based upon belief in hypothetical entities (e.g., simple forms of life that no longer exist; life based upon proto-cells, proto-enzymes, and proto-RNA). These hypothetical entities are required because extant life is so complex that it must have been preceded by simpler forms. You refer to these entities as "imaginary," claiming that they are not observable evidence. You then argue that the complexity of known life is strong evidence for God or an intelligent cause. This is hypocritical because God cannot be observed and therefore is similarly hypothetical and "imaginary."

Response: There is a very fundamental difference in how the opposing hypotheses are supported by evidence. For the hypothesis that God had nothing to do with the start of life, the imaginary entities are invoked to support the hypothesis. The observable evidence (i.e., the twelve steps of the Stairway to Life) all suggest that abiogenesis is an extraordinarily remote possibility. The imaginary "proto-life entities" are called upon to salvage the likelihood of abiogenesis.

In contrast, the hypothesis that God was involved in the start of life is based upon observable evidence (i.e., the twelve steps of the Stairway to Life). Although God is not directly observable, the evidence of the requirement for God to start life and the evidence of layers upon layers of functional information that could only be produced by an intelligent agent are quite observable.

Objection: Your book is discouraging to origin-of-life research. More research is needed, not an end to the research, as you suggest. We simply need more time and more funding to address the concerns that you raise.

Response: When origin-of-life research starts with the assumption of methodological naturalism, it risks leading us away from the truth. More research only risks leading us further away from the truth. Although there may be some side benefits to origin-of-life research, such as the discovery of new laboratory methods to synthesize DNA or proteins, that research need not be conducted under the guise of origin-of-life research. To our knowledge, research funding in the areas of alchemy and perpetual-motion machines have largely disappeared because we have recognized that they are not good research investments. The same needs to be said for origin-of-life research.

Acknowledgments

We are deeply indebted to numerous reviewers whose comments and suggestions greatly enhanced the manuscript: Eric Anderson, John Calvert, Sal Cordova, Daniel Czech, Joe Deweese, Jayme Durant, Ken Fischer, Ken Funk, Berkley Gryder, Doyle Holbird, Lining Huang, Xinli Liao, Cheresse Nartey, Don Slinger, Collin Smith, Joe Styer, Rick Swindell, Wei Wu, Ruth Wu, and three anonymous reviewers. Their generous service as reviewers does not imply their full agreement with the contents, and any remaining errors are our sole responsibility. We would also like to thank Nathan Lindquist for the cover design, Ryan Pickett and Berkley Gryder for figure graphics, and Elite Authors for their expert service in manuscript editing and layout.

antibiotic resistance gene: A gene that enables its host bacteria to grow on a medium containing an antibiotic. Genes encoding resistance to antibiotics ampicillin and tetracycline were used in the cloning experiments of the Venter team.

antisense RNA: RNA complementary to an mRNA sequence.

base pair: A pair of complementary nucleotides that forms a "rung" of the double-helix "ladder" of DNA.

chirality: A property of a molecular structure such that the molecule and its mirror image are not superimposable.

codon: A triplet of nucleotides that specifies a single amino acid or a command to start or stop translation.

DNA: Deoxyribonucleic acid, a polymeric molecule made of nucleotides that are composed of deoxyribose sugar, adenine (A), cytosine (C), guanine (G), or thymine (T), and phosphate groups.

DNA methylation: A temporary modification of either cytosine or adenine bases by the addition of a methyl group. Methylation can modify the activity of a DNA segment without permanent modification to the DNA sequence.

enzyme: A protein that serves as a catalyst.

eukaryote: An organism consisting of a cell or cells in which the genetic material is DNA in the form of chromosomes contained within a distinct nucleus. Eukaryotes include all living organisms other than bacteria and archaea.

expression of a gene: Transcription and/or translation of a gene inside a cell.

frameshift: A mutation involving insertion or deletion of a number of nucleotides that is not divisible by three. Because each set of three nucleotides specifies a codon, a frameshift mutation results in a completely different translation compared to the original.

functional groups: Portions of an organic molecule (or compound) that take part in chemical reactions in the conditions under consideration.

genetic code: A set of rules to translate groups of three nucleotides of DNA or RNA into the amino acid sequence of proteins.

homeostasis: Maintenance of internal stability despite environmental fluctuations and disruptions.

membrane protein: A protein that interacts with, or is part of, biological membranes.

mRNA or messenger RNA: A type of RNA that carries the code or chemical blueprint for a specific protein. In the early stages of protein synthesis, the mRNA is synthesized from a DNA template during transcription.

natural selection: The differential survival of and/or reproduction of classes of entities that differ in one or more characteristics ([26], 6).

nucleus: The large membrane-bounded organelle in eukaryotes that contains the cell's genetic material in the form of multiple linear DNA molecules organized into structures called chromosomes.

nutrient selectable gene: A gene introduced into a cell that enables the cell to synthesize a nutrient that allows the host organism to survive in a culture medium that does not contain this nutrient.

oligonucleotide: A small linear segment of single-stranded DNA.

origin of replication: A particular sequence in a genome where replication is initiated.

plasmid: A small DNA molecule within a cell that is physically separated from the chromosomal DNA and can replicate independently.

polypeptide: A linear organic polymer consisting of a large number of amino acids bonded together in a chain via α-peptide bonds, forming part of (or the whole of) a protein molecule.

prebiotic: The period before life existed.

prokaryote: A microscopic single-celled organism that has neither a distinct nucleus with a membrane nor other specialized membrane-bound organelles.

promoter: A region of DNA that an RNA polymerase binds to, resulting in the initiation of transcription of a particular gene.

protein: A large biomolecule, or macromolecule, consisting of one or more long chains of amino acids linked via α-peptide bonds. Proteins are polypeptides, but not all polypeptides are proteins. Proteins can be folded into well-defined 3-D structures and perform specific functions, while polypeptides may be unstructured and nonfunctional.

proteinoid: A chemical formed when heating a mixture of amino acids. Amino acids in proteinoids are linked mostly by nonpeptide bonds or non-α-peptide bonds.

racemic mixture: A fifty-fifty mixture of two opposite chiral forms. Abiotic chemical reactions naturally produce racemic mixtures.

reading frame: A specific way of dividing the nucleotides into a set of consecutive, nonoverlapping groups of three nucleotides (codons) to determine the amino acids in the protein encoded by a gene. A segment of DNA has six potential reading frames, three in one direction and three in the opposite direction. The promoter of a gene determines the direction of transcription and thus eliminates three of the six potential reading frames of a gene. The translation machinery chooses the translation starting site and thus determines which reading frame will be used to build the protein encoded.

restriction enzyme: A specialized enzyme that cuts a DNA containing a specific sequence of nucleotides.

ribosome: A molecular machine that synthesizes proteins inside cells by translating messenger RNA.

ribozyme: An RNA that serves as a catalyst.

RNA: Ribonucleic acid, a polymeric molecule made of nucleotides that are composed of ribose sugar, adenine (A), cytosine (C), guanine (G), or uracil (U), and phosphate groups.

selectable marker gene: A gene introduced into cells, especially bacterial or eukaryotic cells in culture, that confers a trait suitable for artificial selection.

sequence of DNA: The order of nucleotides in a DNA.

sequence of protein: The order of amino acids in a protein.

sequence of RNA: The order of nucleotides in an RNA.

sequence space: All the possible arrangements of the amino acids in a polypeptide or the nucleotides in a gene or genome. Most arrangements of nucleotides or amino acids in the sequence space have no function, leaving relatively small regions that are populated by naturally occurring genes or proteins.

synthetic lethality: Simultaneous loss of more than one gene, each of which is nonessential, resulting in death.

transcription: The process of synthesizing an RNA molecule using DNA as a template.

translation: The process of synthesizing a polypeptide based on the nucleotide sequence of a corresponding messenger RNA molecule.

transposon: A movable DNA element that, when inserted at some locations within a gene, will disrupt the function of that gene.

vector: A cloning vector is a small piece of DNA taken from a virus, a plasmid, or a cell, which can be stably maintained in an organism and into which a foreign DNA fragment can be inserted for cloning purposes.

Figure Credits

Cover Design: Nathan Lindquist.

Figure 1: Ryan Picket.

Figure 4: Perhelion, Wikimedia Commons, public domain.

Figure 5: The oligo synthesis cycle was adapted with modification from that of Integrated DNA Technologies. https://www.idtdna.com/pages/decoded/decoded-articles/core-concepts/decoded/2015/12/18/oligo-synthesis-why-idt-leads-the-oligo-industry

Figure 6: Graphic produced by Berkley Gryder, including a modified image of a prokaryote cell from LadyofHats, Wikimedia Commons, public domain.

Figure 7: Adapted with modification from Figures 1 and Figure 3 from *The Cell Membrane* in Anatomy & Physiology (https://courses.lumenlearning.com/suny-ap1/chapter/the-cell-membrane/), Authored by: OpenStax College. Provided by: Rice University. License: CC (Creative Commons).

Figure 9: *Top:* Vaccinationist, Wikimedia Commons, public domain.

Bottom: Public Domain from https://www.flickr.com/photos/22719239@N04/2241322031/

Figure 12: From Figure 1 of [164], which is an open-access article distributed under the terms of the Creative Commons Attribution License (CC BY).

Figure 13: From Figure 6B of [183], an open-access article under the terms of the Creative Commons Attribution 4.0 License.

Figure 14: Images created at RCSB PDB from (PDB ID: 4HEA) with Mol* (JavaScript) [227]. The bottom panel is a modification of Figure 1A of [191], used with permission from Elsevier and Copyright Clearance Center (Biochimica et Biophysica Acta (BBA)—Bioenergetics).

Figure 15: *A.* From Figure 1 of [197], an open-access article under the terms of the Creative Commons. *B.* Image created at RCSB PDB from (PDB ID: 5T4O) with Mol* (JavaScript) [227].

Figure 16: From Figure 1 of [134], used with permission from Oxford University Press and Copyright Clearance Center.

Figure 17: The DNA image was taken by Drs. Bruno Zimm and Ruth Kavenoff, the two original copyright holders. Used with permission from Louis Zimm and Carl Zimm, joint heirs of Prof. Bruno Zimm. The image of *E. coli* is from Rocky Mountain Laboratories, Wikimedia Commons, public domain.

Bibliography

1. Aristotle, *The History of Animals, Book V.* 1910, Oxford: Clarendon Press.

2. Redi, F., *Experiments on the generation of insects.* 1909, Chicago: The Open Court Publishing Company.

3. Darwin, E., *Temple of Nature.* 1803.

4. Schwartz, M., The life and works of Louis Pasteur. *J Appl Microbiol*, 2001. 91(4): 597–601.

5. Darwin, C., from Darwin's letter to the botanist and explorer Joseph D. Hooker, February 1, 1871.

6. Orgel, L. E. and F. H. C. Crick, Anticipating an RNA world. Some past speculations on the origin of life: where are they today? *FASEB Journal*, 1993. 7(1): 238–239.

7. NASA. *PCE3, the Prebiotic Chemistry, and Early Earth Environments Consortium.* http://prebioticchem.info/. [Access date: 8/20/2019]

8. NASA. *New NASA Research Consortium to Tackle Life's Origins.* https://astrobiology.nasa.gov/news/new-nasa-research-consortium-to-tackle-lifes-origins/. [Access date: 8/20/2019]

9. Nye, B., *Undeniable: Evolution and the Science of Creation.* 2014, New York: Saint Martin's Press.

10. Freeman, S., et al., *Biological Science.* 5th ed. 2014, Boston: Pearson.

11. Losos, J., K. Mason, and S. Singer, *Biology.* 8th ed. 2008, Boston: McGraw Hill.

12. Belk, C. and V. B. Maier, *Biology: Science for Life (with Physiology).* 3rd ed. 2010, San Francisco: Benjamin Cummings.

13. Hillis, D., et al., *Principles of Life.* 2nd ed. 2014, Sunderland, MA: Sinauer Associates.

14. Denton, M., *Evolution: A Theory in Crisis.* 1986, Bethesda, Maryland: Adler and Adler Publishers.

15. Pennisi, E., Genomics. Synthetic genome brings new life to bacterium. *Science,* 2010. 328(5981): 958–959.

16. Venter, C., *Watch me unveil "synthetic life."* 2010, TED (Technology, Entertainment and Design).

17. Bedau, M., et al., Life after the synthetic cell. *Nature,* 2010. 465(7297): 422–424.

18. Zenonos, G. and J. E. Kim, Life, and...Neurosurgery after the first "synthetic cell." *Neurosurgery*, 2010. 67(2): N14–15.

19. Ball, P., A synthetic creation story. *Nature*, 2010.

20. Wade, N., Researchers say they created a "synthetic cell." 2010, *The New York Times*.

21. Hotz, R. L., Scientists create synthetic organism. 2010, *The Wall Street Journal*.

22. Gill, V., "Artificial life" breakthrough announced by scientists. 2010, *BBC News*.

23. Bourzac, K., How to make an artificial cell. 2010, *MIT Technology Review*.

24. Kowalski, H., First Self-Replicating Synthetic Bacterial Cell Constructed by J. Craig Venter Institute Researchers. 2010, J. Craig Venter Institute Press Releases.

25. Covey, S. R., *The Seven Habits of Highly Effective People: Restoring the Character Ethic*. 2004, New York: Free Press.

26. Futuyma, D., *Evolution*. 2013, Sunderland, MA: Sinauer Associates, Inc.

27. Simpson, G. G., The world into which Darwin led us. *Science*, 1960. 131: 966–974.

28. Zimmer, C., Scientists are designing artisanal proteins for your body. 2017, *The New York Times*.

29. AlQuraishi, M., End-to-end differentiable learning of protein structure. *Cell Systems*, 2019. 8(4): 292–301 e3.

30. Gibson, D. G., et al., Creation of a bacterial cell controlled by a chemically synthesized genome. *Science*, 2010. 329(5987): 52–56.

31. Koonin, E. V., How many genes can make a cell: the minimal-gene-set concept. *Ann Rev Genomics Hum Genet*, 2000. 1: 99–116.

32. Mushegian, A. R. and E. V. Koonin, A minimal gene set for cellular life derived by comparison of complete bacterial genomes. *Proc Natl Acad Sci U S A*, 1996. 93(19): 10268–10273.

33. Koonin, E. V., Comparative genomics, minimal gene-sets and the last universal common ancestor. *Nat Rev Microbiol*, 2003. 1(2): 127–136.

34. Lagesen, K., D. W. Ussery, and T. M. Wassenaar, Genome update: the 1000th genome—a cautionary tale. *Microbiology*, 2010. 156(Pt 3): 603–608.

35. Hutchison, C. A., et al., Global transposon mutagenesis and a minimal Mycoplasma genome. *Science*, 1999. 286(5447): 2165–2169.

36. Glass, J. I., et al., Essential genes of a minimal bacterium. *Proc Natl Acad Sci U S A*, 2006. 103(2): 425–430.

37. Christen, B., et al., The essential genome of a bacterium. *Mol Syst Biol*, 2011. 7: 528.

38. Forsyth, R. A., et al., A genome-wide strategy for the identification of essential genes in *Staphylococcus aureus. Mol Microbiol,* 2002. 43(6): 1387–1400.

39. Ji, Y., et al., Identification of critical staphylococcal genes using conditional phenotypes generated by antisense RNA. *Science,* 2001. 293(5538): 2266–2269.

40. Herring, C. D., J. D. Glasner, and F. R. Blattner, Gene replacement without selection: regulated suppression of amber mutations in *Escherichia coli. Gene,* 2003. 311: 153–163.

41. Kobayashi, K., et al., Essential *Bacillus subtilis* genes. *Proc Natl Acad Sci U S A,* 2003. 100(8): 4678–4683.

42. Mori, H., et al., Functional genomics of *Escherichia coli* in Japan. *Res Microbiol,* 2000. 151(2): 121–128.

43. Baba, T., et al., Construction of *Escherichia coli* K-12 in-frame, single-gene knockout mutants: the Keio collection. *Mol Syst Biol,* 2006. 2: 2006.0008.

44. Kato, J. and M. Hashimoto, Construction of consecutive deletions of the *Escherichia coli* chromosome. *Mol Syst Biol,* 2007. 3: 132.

45. Tucker, C. L. and S. Fields, Lethal combinations. *Nat Genet,* 2003. 35(3): 204–205.

46. Butland, G., et al., eSGA: *E. coli* synthetic genetic array analysis. *Nat Methods,* 2008. 5(9): 789–795.

47. Suthers, P. F., A. Zomorrodi, and C. D. Maranas, Genome-scale gene/reaction essentiality and synthetic lethality analysis. *Mol Syst Biol*, 2009. 5: 301.

48. Costanzo, M., et al., The genetic landscape of a cell. *Science*, 2010. 327(5964): 425–431.

49. Baryshnikova, A., et al., Genetic interaction networks: toward an understanding of heritability. *Ann Rev Genomics Hum Genet*, 2013. 14: 111–133.

50. Kuzmin, E., et al., Systematic analysis of complex genetic interactions. *Science*, 2018. 360(6386).

51. Hutchison, C. A., III, et al., Design and synthesis of a minimal bacterial genome. *Science*, 2016. 351(6280): aad6253.

52. Fraser, C. M., et al., The minimal gene complement of *Mycoplasma genitalium. Science*, 1995. 270(5235): 397–403.

53. Sinha, N. D., et al., Polymer support oligonucleotide synthesis XVIII: use of beta-cyanoethyl-N,N-dialkylamino-/N-morpholino phosphoramidite of deoxynucleosides for the synthesis of DNA fragments simplifying deprotection and isolation of the final product. *Nucleic Acids Res*, 1984. 12(11): 4539–4557.

54. Beaucage, S. L., Oligodeoxyribonucleotides synthesis: Phosphoramidite approach. *Methods Mol Biol*, 1993. 20: 33–61.

55. *Nucleoside phosphoramidite*, in *https://en.wikipedia.org*.

56. Kosuri, S. and G. M. Church, Large-scale de novo DNA synthesis: technologies and applications. *Nat Methods*, 2014. 11(5): 499–507.

57. Roy, S. and M. Caruthers, Synthesis of DNA/RNA and Their Analogs via Phosphoramidite and H-Phosphonate Chemistries. *Molecules*, 2013. 18(11): 14268–14284.

58. Baker, T. A. and S. P. Bell, Polymerases and the replisome: machines within machines. *Cell*, 1998. 92(3): 295–305.

59. Elzanowski, A. A. and J. Ostell. *The Genetic Codes.* https://www.ncbi.nlm.nih.gov/Taxonomy/Utils/wprintgc. cgi?chapter=tgencodes. [Access date: 8/20/2019].

60. Labroussaa, F., et al., Impact of donor-recipient phylogenetic distance on bacterial genome transplantation. *Nucleic Acids Res*, 2016. 44(17): 8501–8511.

61. Lartigue, C., et al., Creating bacterial strains from genomes that have been cloned and engineered in yeast. *Science*, 2009. 325(5948): 1693–1696.

62. Matuscak, S. T. and C. L. Tan, Who are the parents of *Mycoplasma mycoides* JCVI-syn1.0? *BIO-Complexity*, 2016. 2: 1–5.

63. Haeckel, E., *The History of Creation or The Development of the Earth and its Inhabitants by the Action of Natural Causes.* 3rd ed. Vol. 1. 1883, London: Kegan Paul, Trench & Co.

64. Lane, N., *The Vital Question.* 2016, New York, NY: W. W. Norton & Company.

65. Brown, D., *Origin*. 2017, New York, NY: Doubleday.

66. Pross, A., *What Is Life?* 2012, Oxford: Oxford University Press.

67. Wolchover, N., A New Physics of Life. *Quanta* Magazine, 2014.

68. Sagan, C., The abundance of life-bearing planets. *Bioastronomy News*, 1995. 7: 1–4.

69. Stadler, R., *The Scientific Approach to Evolution: What They Didn't Teach You in Biology*. 2016: CreateSpace Independent Publishing Platform.

70. Orgel, L. E., Prebiotic chemistry and the origin of the RNA world. *Critical Reviews in Biochemistry and Molecular Biology*, 2004. 39(2): 99–123.

71. Miller, S. L., A production of amino acids under possible primitive earth conditions. *Science*, 1953. 117(3046): 528–529.

72. Oparin, A. I., *The Origin of Life*. 1938, New York: MacMillan.

73. Johnson, A. P., et al., The Miller volcanic spark discharge experiment. *Science*, 2008. 322(5900): 404.

74. Bada, J. L., New insights into prebiotic chemistry from Stanley Miller's spark discharge experiments. *Chemical Society Reviews*, 2013. 42(5): 2186–2196.

75. Trail, D., E. B. Watson, and N. D. Tailby, The oxidation state of Hadean magmas and implications for early Earth's atmosphere. *Nature*, 2011. 480(7375): 79–82.

76. Watson, B., Early Earth's atmosphere was similar to present-day one. *Science News*, 2011.

77. Kasting, J. F., Earth's early atmosphere. *Science*, 1993. 259(5097): 920–926.

78. Amend, J. P. and E. L. Shock, Energetics of amino acid synthesis in hydrothermal ecosystems. *Science*, 1998. 281(5383): 1659–1662.

79. Esmaili, S., et al., Glycine formation in CO2:CH4:NH3 ices induced by 0-70 eV electrons. *Journal of Chemical Physics*, 2018. 148(16).

80. Burton, A. S., et al., Understanding prebiotic chemistry through the analysis of extraterrestrial amino acids and nucleobases in meteorites. *Chemical Society Reviews*, 2012. 41(16): 5459–5472.

81. Schmitt-Kopplin, P., et al., High molecular diversity of extraterrestrial organic matter in Murchison meteorite revealed forty years after its fall. *Proc Natl Acad Sci U S A*, 2010. 107(7): 2763–2768.

82. Postberg, F., et al., Macromolecular organic compounds from the depths of Enceladus. *Nature*, 2018. 558(7711): 564–568.

83. Lombard, J., P. Lopez-Garcia, and D. Moreira, The early evolution of lipid membranes and the three domains of life. *Nature Reviews Microbiology*, 2012. 10(7): 507–515.

84. Hargreaves, W. R., S. J. Mulvihill, and D. W. Deamer, Synthesis of phospholipids and membranes in prebiotic conditions. *Nature*, 1977. 266(5597): 78–80.

85. Fiore, M. and P. Strazewski, Prebiotic lipidic amphiphiles and condensing agents on the early Earth. *Life* (Basel), 2016. 6(2).

86. Gilbert, W., The RNA world. *Nature*, 1986. 319: 618.

87. Springsteen, G. and G. F. Joyce, Selective derivatization and sequestration of ribose from a prebiotic mix. *Journal of the American Chemical Society*, 2004. 126(31): 9578–9583.

88. Becker, S., et al., Unified prebiotically plausible synthesis of pyrimidine and purine RNA ribonucleotides. *Science*, 2019. 366(6461): 76–82.

89. Robertson, M. P. and G. F. Joyce, The origins of the RNA world. *Cold Spring Harbor Perspectives in Biology*, 2012. 4(5).

90. Benner, S. A., Paradoxes in the origin of life. *Orig Life Evol Biosph*, 2014. 44(4): 339–343.

91. Brown, J. M. and S. G. Davies, Chemical asymmetric synthesis. *Nature*, 1989. 342(6250): 631–636.

92. Blackmond, D. G., The origin of biological homochirality. *Cold Spring Harbor Perspectives in Biology*, 2010. 2(5): 1–17.

93. Joyce, G. F., et al., Chiral selection in poly(C)-directed synthesis of oligo(G). *Nature*, 1984. 310(5978): 602–604.

94. Konno, R., et al., *D-Amino Acids: A New Frontier in Amino Acid and Protein Research—Practical Methods and Protocols.* 2007, New York: Nova Biomedical Books.

95. Jakschitz, T. A. E. and B. M. Rode, Chemical evolution from simple in-organic compounds to chiral peptides. *Chemical Society Reviews*, 2012. 41: 5484–5489.

96. Cohen, G. N., *Microbial Biochemistry.* 2014: Springer.

97. Horiuchi, T., et al., Amino acids in water samples from deep sea hydrothermal vents at Suiyo Seamount, Izu-Bonin Arc, Pacific Ocean. *Organic Geochemistry*, 2004. 35(10): 1121–1128.

98. Johnson, B. J. and G. H. Miller, Archaeological applications of amino acid racemization. *Archaeometry*, 1997. 39: 265–287.

99. Harold, F. M., *In Search of Cell History: The Evolution of Life's Building Blocks.* 2014: University of Chicago Press.

100. Soai, K., et al., Asymmetric autocatalysis and amplification of enantiomeric excess of a chiral molecule. *Nature*, 1995. 378(6559): 767–768.

101. Viedma, C., Chiral symmetry breaking and complete chiral purity by thermodynamic-kinetic feedback near equilibrium: Implications for the origin of biochirality. *Astrobiology*, 2007. 7(2): 312–319.

102. Klussmann, M., et al., Emergence of solution-phase homochirality via crystal engineering of amino acids. *Journal of the American Chemical Society*, 2007. 129(24): 7657–7660.

103. Hazen, R. M., T. R. Filley, and G. A. Goodfriend, Selective adsorption of L- and D-amino acids on calcite: Implications for biochemical homochirality. *Proc Natl Acad Sci U S A*, 2001. 98(10): 5487–5490.

104. Klabunovskii, E. I., Can enantiomorphic crystals like quartz play a role in the origin of homochirality on Earth? *Astrobiology*, 2001. 1(2): 127–131.

105. Kuroha, M., et al., Chiral supramolecular nanoarchitectures from macroscopic mechanical rotations: effects on enantioselective aggregation behavior of phthalocyanines. *Angew Chem Int Ed*, 2019. 58(51): 18454–18459.

106. Tour, J. Animadversions of a synthetic chemist. http://inference-review.com/article/animadversions-of-a-synthetic-chemist. 2016 [Access date: 8/23/2019].

107. Canavelli, P., S. Islam, and M. W. Powner, Peptide ligation by chemoselective aminonitrile coupling in water. *Nature*, 2019. 571(7766): 546–549.

108. Ts'o, P. O. P., *Bases, Nucleosides, and Nucleotides*, in *Basic Principles in Nucleic Acid Chemistry*. 1974, New York: Academic Press. 453–584.

109. Ts'o, P. O. P., I. S. Melvin, and A. C. Olson, Interaction and association of bases and nucleosides in aqueous solutions. *Journal of the American Chemical Society*, 1963. 85(9): 1289–1296.

110. Lindahl, T., Instability and decay of the primary structure of DNA. *Nature*, 1993. 362(6422): 709–715.

111. Lindahl, T. and B. Nyberg, Rate of depurination of native deoxyribonucleic acid. *Biochemistry*, 1972. 11(19): 3610–3618.

112. Cavalieri, E., et al., Mechanism of DNA depurination by carcinogens in relation to cancer initiation. *IUBMB Life*, 2012. 64(2): 169–179.

113. Adam, Z.R., et al., Estimating the capacity for production of formamide by radioactive minerals on the prebiotic Earth. *Scientific Reports*, 2018. 8(1): 265.

114. Ferris, J. P. and G. Ertem, Montmorillonite catalysis of RNA oligomer formation in aqueous solution. A model for the prebiotic formation of RNA. *J Am Chem Soc*, 1993. 115(26): 12270–12275.

115. Ferris, J. P., Montmorillonite catalysis of 30–50 mer oligonucleotides: laboratory demonstration of potential steps in the origin of the RNA world. *Orig Life Evol Biosph*, 2002. 32(4): 311–332.

116. Ferris, J. P., Montmorillonite-catalyzed formation of RNA oligomers: the possible role of catalysis in the origins of life. *Philos Trans R Soc Lond B Biol Sci*, 2006. 361(1474): 1777–1786.

117. Huang, W. and J. P. Ferris, One-step, regioselective synthesis of up to 50-mers of RNA oligomers by montmorillonite catalysis. *J Am Chem Soc*, 2006. 128(27): 8914–8919.

118. Miyakawa, S. and J. P. Ferris, Sequence- and regioselectivity in the montmorillonite-catalyzed synthesis of RNA. *J Am Chem Soc*, 2003. 125(27): 8202–8208.

119. Ertem, G., R. M. Hazen, and J. P. Dworkin, Sequence analysis of trimer isomers formed by montmorillonite catalysis in the reaction of binary monomer mixtures. *Astrobiology*, 2007. 7(5): 715–722.

120. Coari, K. M., et al., Nucleotide selectivity in abiotic RNA polymerization reactions. *Orig Life Evol Biosph*, 2017. 47(3): 305–321.

121. Kawamura, K. and J. P. Ferris, Clay catalysis of oligonucleotide formation: Kinetics of the reaction of the 5'-phosphorimidazolides of nucleotides with the non-basic heterocycles uracil and hypoxanthine. *Orig Life Evol Biosph*, 1999. 29(6): 563–591.

122. Hud, N. V., et al., Addressing the problems of base pairing and strand cyclization in template-directed synthesis: a case for the utility and necessity of "molecular midwives" and reversible backbone linkages for the origin of proto-RNA. *Chem Biodivers*, 2007. 4(4): 768–783.

123. Costanzo, G., et al., Generation of long RNA chains in water. *J Biol Chem*, 2009. 284(48): 33206–33216.

124. Sponer, J. E., et al., Untemplated nonenzymatic polymerization of 3',5'cGMP: a plausible route to 3',5'-linked oligonucleotides in primordia. *J Phys Chem B*, 2015. 119(7): 2979–2989.

125. Costanzo, G., et al., Non-enzymatic oligomerization of 3',5' Cyclic AMP. *PLOS One*, 2016. 11(11): e0165723.

126. Costanzo, G., et al., Nonenzymatic oligomerization of 3',5'-cyclic CMP induced by proton and UV irradiation hints at a nonfastidious origin of RNA. *ChemBioChem*, 2017. 18(15): 1535–1543.

127. Costanzo, G., et al., Generation of RNA molecules by a base-catalysed click-like reaction. *ChemBioChem*, 2012. 13(7): 999–1008.

128. Morasch, M., et al., Dry polymerization of 3',5'-cyclic GMP to long strands of RNA. *ChemBioChem*, 2014. 15(6): 879–883.

129. Saladino, R., et al., Chemomimesis and molecular Darwinism in action: from abiotic generation of nucleobases to nucleosides and RNA. *Life* (Basel), 2018. 8(2).

130. Temussi, P. A., et al., Structural characterization of thermal prebiotic polypeptides. *J Mol Evol*, 1976. 7(2): 105–110.

131. Fox, S. W. and K. Dose, *Molecular Evolution and the Origin of Life*. 1972: W. H. Freeman & Co Ltd. (2nd ed: 1977, New York: Marcel Dekker Inc.).

132. Simon, M. D., et al., Rapid flow-based peptide synthesis. *ChemBioChem*, 2014. 15(5): 713–720.

133. Mong, S. K., et al., Rapid total synthesis of DARPin pE59 and barnase. *ChemBioChem*, 2014. 15(5): 721–733.

134. Su'etsugu, M., et al., Exponential propagation of large circular DNA by reconstitution of a chromosome-replication cycle. *Nucleic Acids Res*, 2017. 45(20): 11525–11534.

135. Neveu, M., H. J. Kim, and S. A. Benner, The "Strong" RNA world hypothesis: fifty years old. *Astrobiology*, 2013. 13(4): 391–403.

136. Mills, D. R., R. L. Peterson, and S. Spiegelman, An extracellular Darwinian experiment with a self-duplicating nucleic acid molecule. *Proc Natl Acad Sci U S A*, 1967. 58(1): 217–224.

137. Kidmose, R. T., et al., Structure of the Qbeta replicase, an RNA-dependent RNA polymerase consisting of viral and host proteins. *Proc Natl Acad Sci U S A*, 2010. 107(24): 10884–10889.

138. Oehlenschläger, F. and M. Eigen, Thirty years later—a new approach to Sol Spiegelman's and Leslie Orgel's in vitro EVOLUTIONARY STUDIES dedicated to Leslie Orgel on the occasion of his seventieth birthday. *Orig Life Evol Biosph*, 1997. 27(5): 437–457.

139. Jia, T. Z., et al., Oligoarginine peptides slow strand annealing and assist non-enzymatic RNA replication. *Nat Chem*, 2016. 8(10): 915–921.

140. Jia, T. Z., et al., Retraction: Oligoarginine peptides slow strand annealing and assist non-enzymatic RNA replication. *Nat Chem*, 2017. 9(12): 1286.

141. Ekland, E. H. and D. P. Bartel, RNA-catalyzed RNA polymerization using nucleoside triphosphates. *Nature*, 1996. 382(6589): 373–376.

142. Horning, D. P. and G. F. Joyce, Amplification of RNA by an RNA polymerase ribozyme. *Proc Natl Acad Sci U S A*, 2016. 113(35): 9786–9791.

143. Attwater, J., et al., Ribozyme-catalyzed RNA synthesis using triplet building blocks. *eLife*, 2018. 7.

144. Lincoln, T. A. and G. F. Joyce, Self-sustained replication of an RNA enzyme. *Science*, 2009. 323(5918): 1229–1232.

145. Szostak, J. Jack Szostak (Harvard/HHMI) part 3: Non-enzymatic copying of nucleic acid templates. https://www.youtube.com/watch?v=jfq5-i8xoIU&t. 2012 [Access date: 8/23/2019].

146. Axe, D. D., Estimating the prevalence of protein sequences adopting functional enzyme folds. *Journal of Molecular Biology*, 2004. 341(5): 1295–1315.

147. Reidharr-Olson, J. F. and R. T. Sauer, Functionally acceptable substitutions in two α-helical regions of repressor. *Proteins: Structure, Function, and Bioinformatics*, 1990. 7(4): 306–316.

148. England, J. L., Statistical physics of self-replication. *J Chem Phys*, 2013. 139(12): 121923.

149. Somerville, R., The Trp repressor, a ligand-activated regulatory protein. *Prog Nucleic Acid Res Mol Biol*, 1992. 42: 1–38.

150. Winkler, W. C., et al., Control of gene expression by a natural metabolite-responsive ribozyme. *Nature*, 2004. 428(6980): 281–286.

151. Pleska, M., et al., Bacterial autoimmunity due to a restriction-modification system. *Current Biology*, 2016. 26(3): 404–409.

152. Kedzierska, B. and F. Hayes, Emerging roles of toxin-antitoxin modules in bacterial pathogenesis. *Molecules*, 2016. 21(6).

153. Horak, R. and H. Tamman, Desperate times call for desperate measures: benefits and costs of toxin-antitoxin systems. *Current Genetics*, 2016: 1–6.

154. Otsuka, Y., Prokaryotic toxin-antitoxin systems: novel regulations of the toxins. *Current Genetics*, 2016. 62(2): 379–382.

155. Page, R. and W. Peti, Toxin-antitoxin systems in bacterial growth arrest and persistence. *Nat Chem Biol*, 2016. 12(4): 208–214.

156. Lindahl, T., DNA repair enzymes acting on spontaneous lesions in DNA. In: *DNA Repair Processes*, W. Nichols and D. Murphy, Editors. 1977, Miami: Symposia Specialists. 225–240.

157. Ames, B. N., M. K. Shigenaga, and T. M. Hagen, Oxidants, antioxidants, and the degenerative diseases of aging. *Proc Natl Acad Sci U S A*, 1993. 90(17): 7915–7922.

158. Tice, R. and R. Setlow, DNA repair and replication in aging organisms and cells, in *Handbook of the Biology of Aging*, E. Finch and E. Schneider, Editors. 1985, New York: Van Nostrand Reinhold. 173–224.

159. Haber, J. E., DNA recombination: the replication connection. *Trends in Biochemical Sciences*, 1999. 24(7): 271–275.

160. Klug, W., et al., *Concepts of Genetics.* 11th ed. 2015, England: Pearson Education Inc.

161. Syed, A. and J. A. Tainer, The MRE11-RAD50-NBS1 complex conducts the orchestration of damage signaling and outcomes to stress in DNA replication and repair. *Annu Rev Biochem*, 2018. 87: 263–294.

162. Lindahl, T., Suppression of spontaneous mutagenesis in human cells by DNA base excision-repair. *Mutat Res*, 2000. 462(2–3): 129–135.

163. Grossman, L. and A. T. Yeung, The UvrABC endonuclease system of Escherichia coli—a view from Baltimore. *Mutat Res*, 1990. 236(2–3): 213–221.

164. Nickson, C. M. and J. L. Parsons, Monitoring regulation of DNA repair activities of cultured cells in-gel using the comet assay. *Frontiers in Genetics*, 2014. 5.

165. Knoch, J., et al., Rare hereditary diseases with defects in DNA-repair. *Eur J Dermatol*, 2012. 22(4): 443–455.

166. Hoeijmakers, J. H., Genome maintenance mechanisms for preventing cancer. *Nature*, 2001. 411(6835): 366–374.

167. Hoeijmakers, J. H., DNA damage, aging, and cancer. *N Engl J Med*, 2009. 361(15): 1475–1485.

168. Eigen, M., Self-organization of matter and evolution of biological macromolecules. *Naturwissenschafteni*, 1971. 58: 465–523.

169. Parker, J., et al., *Brock Biology of Microorganisms*. 10th ed. 2003, Englewood Cliffs, NJ: Prentice Hall.

170. Lasic, D. D., The mechanism of vesicle formation. *Biochem J*, 1988. 256(1): 1–11.

171. Mansy, S. S., Membrane transport in primitive cells. *Cold Spring Harb Perspect Biol*, 2010. 2(8): a002188.

172. Gershfeld, N. L., The critical unilamellar lipid state: a perspective for membrane bilayer assembly. *Biochim Biophys Acta*, 1989. 988(3): 335–350.

173. Ginsberg, L., D. L. Gilbert, and N. L. Gershfeld, Membrane bilayer assembly in neural tissue of rat and squid as a critical phenomenon: influence of temperature and membrane proteins. *J Membr Biol*, 1991. 119(1): 65–73.

174. Tremper, K. E. and N. L. Gershfeld, Temperature dependence of membrane lipid composition in early blastula embryos of Lytechinus pictus: selective sorting of phospholipids into nascent plasma membranes. *J Membr Biol*, 1999. 171(1): 47–53.

175. Jin, A. J., et al., A singular state of membrane lipids at cell growth temperatures. *Biochemistry*, 1999. 38(40): 13275–13278.

176. Thomas, J. A. and F. R. Rana, The influence of environmental conditions, lipid composition, and phase behavior on the origin of cell membranes. *Orig Life Evol Biosph*, 2007. 37(3): 267–285.

177. Alberts, B., et al., *Molecular Biology of the Cell*. 4th ed. 2002, New York: Garland Science.

178. Poetsch, A. and D. Wolters, Bacterial membrane proteomics. *Proteomics*, 2008. 8(19): 4100–4122.

179. Takata, K., T. Matsuzaki, and Y. Tajika, Aquaporins: water channel proteins of the cell membrane. *Prog Histochem Cytochem*, 2004. 39(1): 1–83.

180. Gonen, T. and T. Walz, The structure of aquaporins. *Q Rev Biophys*, 2006. 39(4): 361–396.

181. Murata, K., et al., Structural determinants of water permeation through aquaporin-1. *Nature*, 2000. 407(6804): 599–605.

182. Holland, I. B., et al., *ABC Proteins: From Bacteria to Man*. 2003, London: Academic Press.

183. Husada, F., et al., Conformational dynamics of the ABC transporter McjD seen by single-molecule FRET. *The EMBO Journal*, 2018. 37(21).

184. Driessen, A. J. and N. Nouwen, Protein translocation across the bacterial cytoplasmic membrane. *Annu Rev Biochem*, 2008. 77: 643–667.

185. Akopian, D., et al., Signal recognition particle: an essential protein-targeting machine. *Annu Rev Biochem*, 2013. 82: 693–721.

186. Dalbey, R. E., et al., The membrane insertase YidC. *Biochim Biophys Acta*, 2014. 1843(8): 1489–1496.

187. Blobel, G., Intracellular protein topogenesis. *Proceedings of the National Academy of Sciences*, 1980. 77(3): 1496.

188. Harold, F. M., Molecules into cells: Specifying spatial architecture. *Microbiology and Molecular Biology Reviews*, 2005. 69(4): 544–564.

189. Szostak, J. Jack Szostak (Harvard/HHMI) Part 2: Protocell Membranes. https://www.youtube.com/watch?v=CJ5jh33OiOA. 2012 [Access date: 8/23/2019].

190. Berg, J., J. Tymoczko, and L. Stryer, *Biochemistry*. 5th ed. 2002, New York: W H Freeman.

191. Berrisford, J. M., R. Baradaran, and L. A. Sazanov, Structure of bacterial respiratory complex I. *Biochim Biophys Acta*, 2016. 1857(7): 892–901.

192. Yang, X. H. and B. L. Trumpower, Purification of a three-subunit ubiquinol-cytochrome c oxidoreductase complex from *Paracoccus denitrificans*. *J Biol Chem*, 1986. 261(26): 12282–12289.

193. Iwata, S., et al., Complete structure of the 11-subunit bovine mitochondrial cytochrome bc1 complex. *Science*, 1998. 281(5373): 64–71.

194. Iwata, S., Structure and function of bacterial cytochrome-*c* oxidase. *J Biochem*, 1998. 123(3): 369–375.

195. Balsa, E., et al., NDUFA4 is a subunit of complex IV of the mammalian electron Transport Chain. *Cell Metabolism*, 2012. 16(3): 378–386.

196. Ahmad, Z., F. Okafor, and T. F. Laughlin, Role of charged residues in the catalytic sites of *Escherichia coli* ATP synthase. *J Amino Acids*, 2011. 2011: 785741.

197. Sobti, M., et al., Cryo-EM structures of the autoinhibited *E. coli* ATP synthase in three rotational states. *eLife*, 2016. 5.

198. Stewart_Lab, ATP synthase: structure and function. 2016 [Access date: 11/30/2019].

199. Yasuda, R., et al., Resolution of distinct rotational substeps by submillisecond kinetic analysis of F1-ATPase. *Nature*, 2001. 410(6831): 898–904.

200. Weber, J. and A. E. Senior, ATP synthesis driven by proton transport in F1F0-ATP synthase. *FEBS Letters*, 2003. 545(1): 61–70.

201. Breuer, M., et al., Essential metabolism for a minimal cell. *eLife*, 2019. 8.

202. Bellon, S., et al., Crystal structures of *Escherichia coli* topoisomerase IV ParE subunit (24 and 43 kilodaltons): a single residue dictates differences in novobiocin potency against topoisomerase IV and DNA gyrase. *Antimicrob Agents Chemother*, 2004. 48(5): 1856–1864.

203. Luo, H., et al., DEG 10, an update of the database of essential genes that includes both protein-coding genes and noncoding genomic elements. *Nucleic Acids Res*, 2014. 42(Database issue): D574–D580.

204. Zhang, R. and Y. Lin, DEG 5.0, a database of essential genes in both prokaryotes and eukaryotes. *Nucleic Acids Res*, 2009. 37(Database issue): D455–D458.

205. Tropp, B. E., *Molecular Biology: Genes to Proteins*. 4th ed. 2012, Sudbury, MA: Jones & Bartlett Learning, LLC.

206. Earnest, T. M., et al., Ribosome biogenesis in replicating cells: Integration of experiment and theory. *Biopolymers*, 2016. 105(10): 735–751.

207. Crick, F. H., The origin of the genetic code. *J Mol Biol*, 1968. 38(3): 367–379.

208. Koonin, E. V. and A. S. Novozhilov, Origin and evolution of the genetic code: the universal enigma. *IUBMB Life*, 2009. 61(2): 99–111.

209. Milo, R. and R. Phillips, *Cell Biology by the Numbers*. 2015, New York: Garland Science.

210. Harvey, S. H., M. J. Krien, and M. J. O'Connell, Structural maintenance of chromosomes (SMC) proteins, a family of conserved ATPases. *Genome Biol*, 2002. 3(2): REVIEWS3003.

211. Wang, X., P. Montero Llopis, and D. Z. Rudner, Organization and segregation of bacterial chromosomes. *Nat Rev Genet*, 2013. 14(3): 191–203.

212. Tompa, P. and G. D. Rose, The Levinthal paradox of the interactome. *Protein Sci*, 2011. 20(12): 2074–2079.

213. Steele, E. J., et al., Cause of Cambrian explosion—terrestrial or cosmic? *Progress in Biophysics and Molecular Biology*, 2018. 136: 3–23.

214. Wald, G., The origin of life. *Scientific American*, 1954: 46–48.

215. Urey, H. C., in *Christian Science Monitor*. 1962. 4.

216. Nagel, T., *The Last Word*. 1997, Oxford University Press.

217. Dawkins, R., *The Selfish Gene*. 1989, New York Oxford University Press.

218. Schrödinger, E., *What is life?* 1943, Cambridge, UK: Cambridge University Press.

219. Deutsch, D. and C. Marletto, Constructor theory of information. *Proc Math Phys Eng Sci*, 2015. 471(2174): 20140540.

220. Sample, I. I predict a great revolution: inside the struggle to define life. https://www.theguardian.com/science/2019/jan/26/i-predict-great-revolution-physicists-define-life-paul-davies. 2019 [Access date: February 2, 2019].

221. Walker, S. I. and P. C. Davies, The algorithmic origins of life. *J R Soc Interface*, 2013. 10(79): 20120869.

222. Zemach, H. and M. Zemach, *The Judge: An Untrue Tale*. Sunburst Book. 1988: Farrar, Straus and Giroux (BYR).

223. Parke, E. C., Flies from meat and wasps from trees: Reevaluating Francesco Redi's spontaneous generation experiments. *Stud Hist Philos Biol Biomed Sci*, 2014. 45: 34–42.

224. Deichmann, U., Origin of life. The role of experiments, basic beliefs, and social authorities in the controversies about the spontaneous generation of life and the subsequent debates about synthesizing life in the laboratory. *Hist Philos Life Sci*, 2012. 34(3): 341–359.

225. Lartigue, C., et al., Genome transplantation in bacteria: changing one species to another. *Science*, 2007. 317(5838): 632–638.

226. Gabius, H. J. and J. Roth, An introduction to the sugar code. *Histochem Cell Biol*, 2017. 147(2): 111–117.

227. Sehnal, D., et al., Mol*: towards a common library and tools for web molecular graphics. *MolVA '18 Proceedings of the Workshop on Molecular Graphics and Visual Analysis of Molecular Data*, 2018: 29–33.

INDEX

A

C

D

E

F

Fanconi anemia 137
fatty acid 76
fermentation 150, 193
ferricyanide 96, 105
First Amendment of the US Constitution 14, 189-190
fitness 57, 124
solid phase peptide synthesis 105
Food and Drug Administration (FDA) 72
formaldehyde 80, 81
formamide 98
formose 80
Fox, Sydney 104
frameshift 53, 220
Free Exercise Clause (of the US Constitution) 190
frozen accident hypothesis 166
furnace 128

G

Gelsinger, Jesse 25
general secretion pathway 146
genetic code 23, 24, 46, 48, 166-167, 220
genotype 109, 119, 127, 161, 174
Gilbert, Walter 108
glmS gene 130
glycerol 76, 89-90
God of the gaps 214
GTP 146

H

Haeckel, Ernst 61, 63-65, 70, 194
Haemophilus influenzae 27

About The Authors

Change Laura Tan received a BS in chemistry from Hunan Normal University, an MS in organic chemistry from Nan Kai University, and a PhD in biochemistry from University of Pennsylvania, and also completed postdoctoral training in genetics at Harvard Medical School. She is currently an associate professor of biological sciences at the University of Missouri. Her research interests include genetics, developmental biology, molecular biology, origin of life, and origin of biodiversity. She teaches molecular biology, signal transduction, and general biology to graduate and undergraduate students.

Photo Credit:
Michael Dodd

Rob Stadler is the author of *The Scientific Approach to Evolution: What They Didn't Teach You in Biology.* He received a BS in biomedical engineering from Case Western Reserve University, an MS in electrical engineering from MIT, and a PhD in medical engineering from the Harvard/MIT Division of Health Sciences and Technology. As a scientist in the medical device industry for over twenty years, he has obtained more than 140 US patents, has been elected fellow of the American Institute of Medical and Biomedical Engineers, and has contributed to medical devices that are implanted in millions of patients worldwide.

The authors can be reached at scientificevolution.com@gmail.com or by visiting www.scientificevolution.com.

Also from Rob Stadler:

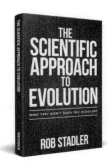

For more than 150 years, continuous debate has swirled around the topic of evolution. From Darwin to Dawkins, extensive scientific evidence has been presented for evolution, yet almost half of contemporary society still isn't convinced. *The Scientific Approach to Evolution: What They Didn't Teach You in Biology* provides a rational new perspective on this debate. Scientific evidence is not all created equally. Some forms of evidence only provide low confidence, while other forms of evidence provide high confidence. Rob Stadler describes a compelling approach to determine the level of confidence and applies it to the commonly cited evidence for evolution. When high-confidence evidence is appropriately prioritized over low-confidence evidence, the result is a profound new view of evolution—one that they did not teach you in biology.

Made in the USA
Columbia, SC
02 October 2021